HAT BOXES and BANDBOXES
at Shelburne Museum

Hat Boxes
and
BANDBOXES
at Shelburne Museum

By Lilian Baker Carlisle

Museum Pamphlet Series, number 4

PUBLISHED BY

THE SHELBURNE MUSEUM

SHELBURNE • VERMONT

PUBLICATIONS ISSUED BY SHELBURNE MUSEUM

The Story of the Shelburne Museum

The Story of the Ticonderoga

Life in the Colchester Reef Lighthouse

PAMPHLET SERIES:

No. 1.—The Carriages at Shelburne Museum

No. 2.—Pieced Work and Applique Quilts at Shelburne Museum

No. 3.—Woodworking Tools at Shelburne Museum

No. 4.—Hat Boxes and Bandboxes at Shelburne Museum

PRINTED IN THE UNITED STATES OF AMERICA
BY THE LANE PRESS, BURLINGTON, VERMONT

Bandbox Room

"A Peep at the Moon" bandbox see page 195

BANDBOXES—*American Art Stated in the Vernacular*

"Trivial circumstances, which show the manners of the age, are often more instructive as well as entertaining, than the great transactions of wars and negotiations, which are nearly similar in all periods and in all countries of the world."

DAVID HUME, 1711–76, Scot historian and philosopher

PROBABLY if one has contemplated hat boxes or bandboxes at all, he has simply thought of them as repositories for hats and dismissed them as of no importance—expendable trifles that today come with expensive hats at no extra charge.

The collection of bandboxes on display at the Shelburne Museum will point up that these "trifles" existed in the past as evidence of the deep wanderlust in the heart of a mobile American population. They also mirror a restless nation's high standard of living at a very early period of its history. It is true that bandboxes exist in other countries, but nowhere are they found in such abundance and variety as they are met with in America.

We tend to remember bandboxes as feminine adjuncts in which the ladies stored their fine bonnets, huge calaches, with their wired accordian folds and down-filled quilted satin "pumpkin hoods." Originally the bandbox was used by both men and women to store and carry about the elaborate starched ruffs we see in old portraits. When the stiff ruff went out of fashion, men adopted a soft flat lace collar (*Samuel Pepys' Diary* mentions that in 1662 he put on his first "lace-band" which set off everything else in his costume). The narrow linen band came into vogue next and we still see the echo of this fashion in the cleric collar.

Ladies used the boxes not only for their bonnets, but as portable storage compartments for ribbons, artificial flowers and hair pieces, dresses, jewelry and the thousand and one bagatelles so dear to the feminine heart. Bandboxes in their progressive sizes were the forerunners of the nested or self-storing luggage considered so new, smart and modern today.

The period of greatest popularity of the bandbox was the second quarter of the 19th century. Unfamiliar forms of transportation—the steamboat, canal boat and railroad train—were being promoted all over the country. This period also coincided with an interesting variety of new conditions in our country's economic development.

The first circumstance was the acceptance of a female labor force in factories. Eli Whitney's invention of the cotton gin erased all past concepts regarding the amount of available raw cotton separated from seeds and ready for spinning into textiles. Because of mechanical improvements to the spinning frames and jennies themselves, the amount of finished cloth turned out was also greatly increased. Finally, brute force was no longer necessary to run the looms because of the addition of steam and water power. Now jobs formerly held by strong men could be performed by slim young girls, and this untapped pool of labor supplied the mills that mushroomed overnight. Girls from all over New England swarmed to the textile centers and with part of their wages purchased pretty, stylish clothes. Storage containers were needed to protect these new wardrobes, and bandboxes were required for their frequent trips home. Bandboxes were luxuries every girl could afford—the best quality wooden ones in the mammoth size cost only 50¢ and the more diminutive ones sold for 12¢. Multiple boxes were purchased, and girls collected boxes in various sizes just as today they try to amass sets of matched luggage.

Another section of our population was also ready for travel at this time. With the wars over and money jingling in their pockets, hard-working middle-class Americans decided it was time to get "culture" and to pay homage to the historical shrines where their parents had met the enemy and pushed them from our country. First-class hotels sprang up. Here a man could live like a king and almost everyone could afford a short holiday or make an excuse to go to the "city" on business. At this moment in time, Americans also discovered the beauty of our native scenery. The "Fashionable or Northern Tour" became immensely popular.

> The oppressive heat of summer in the southern section of the U.S. and the consequent exposure to illness, have long induced the wealthy part of our population to seek at that season of the year, the more salubrious climate of the north. But the recent gigantic internal improvements in the northern and middle states and development of new and highly interesting natural scenery, together with the increased facilities for travelling, have greatly augmented the number of tourists within a short period. The railroads, canals, coal mines, the Springs, the Falls, the Lakes, the fortifications of Quebec, the sublime mountain scenery in New York and New England, with the various attractions presented in the large commercial cities, cannot fail of insuring to a traveller a rich compensation for the toils incident to a journey.
>
> Traveller's Guide Through the Middle and Northern States
> by G. M. DAVISON, published 1833.

Thus the need for bandboxes is attested to. It seems strange, however, that such a slight, fragile trifle as a paper-covered pasteboard box would have lasted all these decades. Over the years, many have been destroyed, of course, but where there was space in an attic or other undisturbed place, the box still served a useful purpose as a storage container, and so was protected and preserved. Fortunately for us there appeared on the scene at this time an ardent collector of Americana, and it is he who has been credited with having "discovered" the early American bandbox.

Mr. Alexander W. Drake studied to become an artist, but through his knowledge of woodblock methods of reproduction turned to magazine publication. He was art director of *Scribner's* Magazine from the issuance of its first number in 1870 until it became *The Century* Magazine in 1881 and from that time continuously until his retirement in 1914. During this period American wood engraving reached a standard which was acknowledged unexcelled either in this country or abroad. Through Drake's powerful influence and through recognition in *Scribner's* and *The Century*, work of the foremost artists and illustrators of his day and time was made known and published.

Mr. Drake was interested in many other aspects of Americana and collected extensively. Part One of the 1913 sales catalog of *The Famous Collections formed by Mr. A. W. Drake* issued for the public sale under the management of the American Art Association listed 2039 examples of "antique samplers and needlework, fragments of old printed chintz, bandboxes and wallpapers, glass bottles, pottery, china, pewter, engraved pledge glasses, antique silver cups and ladles, an extraordinary collection of old finger rings, silver, enameled and pearl snuff boxes, patch boxes and vinaigrettes, old paintings and prints."

At the second afternoon's sale held March 11, 1913, sixty bandboxes were offered and described. The following evening fifty-two bandboxes were listed for sale. An unpublished biographical sketch written by Mrs. Edith True Drake mentions that her husband had started on his quest for bandboxes around the turn of the 20th century.

Old-time bandboxes possessed many qualities which naturally appealed to one who had spent his life in helping to develop American wood engraving and illustration, for the pictures on bandboxes were drawn expressly for that purpose, engraved on wood blocks, and printed by hand in three or more colors

Back of wood block showing two indentations for holding or lifting block 12 x 9½".

Face of carved wood block, showing swag and tassel design. This block was used for stamping wall paper.

after the manner of Japanese prints, but of course more crudely. These band-box prints record a definite and individual phase of early American pictorial art and represent some of the first color printing done in this country. Some of the earliest papers may have come from France, as did our first wall papers, but later the pictures are characteristically American in subject and treatment. The drawing was invariably strong, the color scheme decorative, with well-designed mass effect and elimination of unnecessary detail. . . . The paint used was "gouache," opaque color, and this may account for the fact that so many of the prints have retained much of their original tone. The backgrounds showed a wide range of colors, but each was invariably a smooth unbroken tone, on which the design in three colors, was printed from three blocks. The backgrounds were rich, cerulean blue and lighter shades—soft, tapestry-like green, and a variety of yellows, from Mandarin or lemon-yellow to soft buff and canary shades. The designs were printed in soft reds, dull pink, brown, olive green and white. The high-lights were printed last, of course, and were opaque white. Some of these effects have been—not faded, but softened by time to what a lover of these delectable prints has called "dream colors."

In fewer than ten years, Mr. Drake had collected nearly 300 of these American bandboxes. The majority had come from the attics of homes in scattered New England villages. In his leisurely rambles, he would secure the friendly and helpful interest of the postmaster, village doctor or store keeper and soon his quest would be known. Other boxes were gathered from New York and Pennsylvania.

Where the boxes were in good condition, they were not defaced by cutting, but many had suffered from leaky attic roofs and the tops were either badly stained or had almost disintegrated from moisture. The idea of mounting the surviving portions of the boxes on sturdy panels served two purposes. It showed off to advantage the entire design and protected the remains of the box.

Stimulated by Mr. Drake's collecting, Cooper Union and one or two other museums evidenced interest in bandboxes as a wallpaper design source. An even fewer number of private collectors had begun to adapt the bandboxes to decorative purposes in their homes. One of the first of these collectors was Mrs. J. Watson Webb who conceived the unique idea of utilizing the bandboxes and tops to panel the walls of two bedrooms in her Long Island home. The tops were framed and used as a frieze below the ceiling. When she closed this house, her son, J. Watson Webb, Jr., asked for the "hat box rooms" and today these framed bandboxes and tops are a part of his home in Los Angeles, California.

Mrs. Webb augmented her bandbox collection over the next forty years and consequently today at Shelburne Museum, a group of almost 200 band-boxes and more than 100 panels and tops are on view to the public.

No longer is it easy to find bandboxes in good condition. A collection of boxes has never been a simple exhibit to display because of its bulk, but the Hat Box Room in the Hat and Fragrance Unit at the Shelburne Museum has been described by connoisseurs and casual visitors alike as one of the choice displays created by Mrs. J. Watson Webb, founder and president of the museum.

Should you be fortunate enough to own a bandbox or to find one you can acquire, it is hoped you will bring it from obscurity and place it on display. Its straightforward coloring and designs of historical interest will enrich your life and bring added enjoyment and pleasure to those who visit in your home.

LILIAN BAKER CARLISLE
June 9, 1959

The Webb hat box rooms in their Long Island setting

Table of Contents

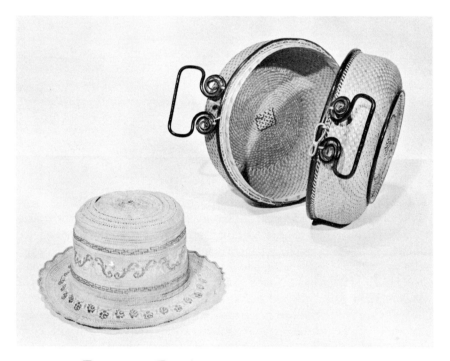

Bonnet Basket and Straw Hat

The woven basket, measuring 8″ in diameter is in natural color and trim is black painted reed bent to shape. Child-size woven straw hat is just under 5″ high and nests inside the basket. Colored designs on the hat have been worked in tent stitching, using the straw as a canvas for the needlework. Date is unknown.   No. 167

Bandboxes come in a variety of sizes and Mrs. J. Watson Webb, President of the Shelburne Museum (at right) compares one of the intermediate examples with the trinket box held by Mrs. Lilian Carlisle.

BANDBOX ROOM

HAT AND FRAGRANCE UNIT

The Hat and Fragrance Unit is considered by authorities and the visiting public, both male and female, to be one of the most entrancing exhibits at the Shelburne Museum. Here in a tasteful and unusual surrounding are exhibited the fine examples of embroidery, needlework, more than 300 quilts and woven coverlets, fine hooked rugs, feminine bibelots and accessories. Here also in the bandbox room is the extraordinary collection of over 200 bandboxes collected by Mrs. Webb over a period of 40 years. The walls are hung with bandbox panels, waist-high glass-topped tables are piled high with boxes and below the tables, arranged in stair-step precision are stacks of additional boxes. A birdseye maple simulated store-front window and recessed wall niches display the collection of manikin heads adorned with bonnets, caps and hats.

The Hat and Fragrance Unit is only one of the 26 structures on the 40 acres comprising the Shelburne Museum. Located on Route 7, just seven miles south of Burlington, Vermont, this non-profit educational institution founded in 1947 by Mr. and Mrs. J. Watson Webb is open each year from the last week in May until mid-October.

AUNT HANNAH
The Bandbox Maker

Anyone collecting hat boxes hopes to have a chance to acquire at least one of the Hannah Davis bandboxes. Fortunately for us, this Jaffrey, New Hampshire woman possessed qualities so inspiring and a personality so endearing that her life and work have been well documented for us. An article written by Margaret C. Robinson which was published in a Boston newspaper in 1925 and an address given before the Jaffrey Village Improvement Society by Mr. Albert Annett, a local antiquarian, furnish us with the facts of this esteemed lady's background.

Hannah Davis, born in 1784, was descended from self-reliant, sturdy pioneer stock. Her grandfather, John Eaton, came from Bedford, Massachusetts to Jaffrey in 1774, just one year after the town itself was incorporated. He was a millwright by trade, but his skills encompassed many other fields. His old account book gives evidence of some of the work he tackled as a matter of course. His knowledge of spelling was perfunctory, but adequate and he worked out his own system of phonetic writing. The journal shows that he made flax wheels and repaired big wheels (wool wheels) and that he "dugg graves," made carts, "tuggs," "collers," "Corfens" and sleds, as well as leach tubs, "ches pres" and "exaltrees." This working in wood was evidently a trait he handed down in his family.

Peter Davis, Hannah's father, was a maker of wooden clocks, but he died when Hannah was a young woman. Somewhat later, in 1818, her mother died, leaving the thirty-four-year-old spinster to make her own way in a world where few job opportunities for women existed.

With typical Yankee resourcefulness, Hannah surveyed the field. She remembered the hours she had watched her father dexterously carving out the meshing wheels and other working parts of his clocks. Her memory also probably retained a picture of her grandfather shaping up his "exaltrees and ches presses." She resolved to go into the business of fabricating wooden hat boxes.

In his address, Mr. Annett described Hannah's methods of work— "She would look about in the woods until she found a fine big spruce tree suited to her purpose. She would then visit the owner of the woods and make terms with him for the purchase of the tree. She would hire a man to cut down the tree and haul it to her house. The log was cut into appropriate lengths, and these stood on end on a wooden platform. She had invented a machine, run by foot power (and it took a strong man to run it) operating a sharp blade, which neatly cut off vertically a thin slice from the log about an eighth of an inch thick, for the sides of the bandboxes. These were called scabboards. The first slices were of course not very wide; from these she made her little bandboxes, suitable for ribbons and trinkets. Some of these were only five inches high. As the slices grew wider, the bandboxes grew larger, and some were fully as capacious as large suitcases of the present day. For the bottoms and covers of the boxes, she used pine, of a little greater thickness, as the wood need not be bent."

The boxes were all lined with newspapers. Hannah made bargains with her friends and neighbors, and in payment for the papers they saved up for her, she allowed them to choose bandboxes from her finished products. The same barter system was used in collecting the paper which covered the outside of her boxes. Many of these are covered in a regular repeating floral pattern of hand-blocked wall paper. Several, however, display sheets of wallpaper featuring episodes and scenes from Napoleon's career. Along with many Americans, it appears that Hannah was sympathetic to the pathos in the life of this exiled military genius. In the Shelburne Museum collection, there is a box depicting Napoleon holding his young son in his arms, and another of her documented bandboxes pictures Napoleon conversing with one of his officers in a battle scene.

At first Hannah tried to dispose of her stock by trading the boxes for her simple needs. Later on she began selling them to the local merchants (50¢ for the big ones, 12¢ for the small size); but this market soon became glutted. Her best customers, she had found, were the young women and teen-age girls who had by 1825–30 begun working in the enormous textile factories in the nearby Merrimack River cities of Lowell, Nashua and Manchester. Although it was not possible for the girls to come to Jaffrey, why not, she asked herself, take the boxes direct to her most lucrative market. The fact that she had no horse of her own was but a small problem, for she discovered she could rent a gentle beast from one of the neighbors. In winter she hitched him to a sleigh, and in summer to her large wagon with its white prairie schooner canopy top. This she piled high with her gay and fresh, bright-colored merchandise and set off. During the factory lunch hour she parked the vehicle outside the gates and soon it was swarming with young girls eager to purchase a brand-new bandbox.

We tend to think of women in factories as a fairly recent phenomenon, but George S. White's *History of the Rise and Progress of the Cotton Manufacture in England and America* published in Philadelphia in 1836 gives us a picture of the great 19th century work-force made up of women. Although factory supervisors realized that children under 10 years of age "proved unprofitable in almost every branch" of their factories, still if the parents worked there and insisted upon it, they would employ children of this age "to do light chores or some very light work, such as setting spools in the frame, or piecing rolls." Boys of 14, they found, were "able in most employments to do the work of men; they only want the skill." At an early date, they recognized that their prize untapped employment pool was woman power. Many girls at 14 were "just as steady and discreet" as others at 16, and furthermore "women are much more ready to follow good regulations and are not captious and do not clan as the men do against their overseers."

Employers preferred the girls and the girls loved working at the factory, for although many had to help their parents support the younger members of the family, yet "It is a fact of common notoriety, that the females employed in factories cloathe better or more expensively than others in similar circumstances as to property, or even than the daughters of our respectable farmers."

This disposition to dress extravagantly, it was discovered, soon abated and the girls began to lay up their wages. It was not unusual for a girl to lay up "$200 to $300 in from three to four years, and thus fit herself and her home out decently when married." Also many of the socially-conscious factories offered educational advantages to the girls in the night schools they ran from 8 to 10 o'clock each evening. Here they could learn writing, arithmetic, grammar, geography and history. Almost all of the factories were very proud of the Sunday Schools they had established and the churches that had sprung up nearby after the factories had been built.

The girls were very well paid for the times. Their wages averaged from $2 to $3 per week. At this time in England a common male laborer received about 74¢ per week, in France between 37¢ and 40¢ and in America $1. In 1827, out of 1200 persons employed in the Lowell cotton mills, nine-tenths of them were females (20 of whom were from 12 to 14 years of age).

When the factory girls left the mill towns for their visits back home they took with them the latest city fashions, and they have been pictured "riding on the tops of the old stage-coaches in their trips to and from their homes with Aunt Hannah's bandboxes around them like satellites around a sun."

In later years Hannah Davis broke her hip. When she was no longer able to support herself, the townspeople tried to out-do one another in taking care of her. The Baptist church, of which she was a charter member, built her a little house; neighbors stopped by and left home-cooked delicacies for her and occasionally one of the men would drive by and dump a load of firewood at her place. Many years later, one of the older residents recalled how he had been one of the lucky "older boys" between 10 and

12 years who had been chosen by his school teacher to go up to Aunt Hannah's one Saturday morning and cut up and stack a load of donated wood for her.

It is no wonder the children loved to visit her house. As a reward for their favors, Hannah was always ready to oblige with a tale of the old days in Jaffrey when there were dense forests, lurking Indians and wild animals. Certainly one of her favorite stories must have related the events of the day the old Meeting House was framed up. According to tradition this Meeting House, one of the finest in New England with a beautiful Christopher Wren tower, was raised on June 17, 1775, the day of the battle of Bunker Hill, and it was said that the men on the job heard the booming of the cannon in the distance. Passed down through the years also was the story that John Eaton, Hannah's grandfather, who had been working on the Meeting House celebrated its completion by standing on his head on the ridge pole. It must have been a wonderful sight—that "gay figure high in the air outlined against the western sky where the sun was setting behind Grand Monadnock."

Hannah Davis died in November of 1863, and so vividly was she remembered in her community that 30 years later, a group of young girls, the "Gold Gatherers," members of a mission band, installed a church window "In Memory of Aunt Hannah Davis."

Hannah Davis Wooden Bandboxes

COCKATOO

This same design of wallpaper has been used to cover the bandbox illustrated on page 66. New Hampshire newspapers and a copy of the *Massachusetts Spy* line the inside of the box. Advertisements in these papers date from 1824, 1827, 1826 and 1830. A notice pasted inside the top of the box reprints under date of Feb. 6, 1832 a news item from the *Boston Courier*.

Red, white and green varnish on blue background

Oval 15 x 13, 11½" deep   No. 136   Circa 1832

SWAN HANDLE FRUIT BASKET

Handsome fruit basket design is encircled with chalk white foliage forms. Newspapers lining the box include *Christian Register and Boston Observer*, August 13, 1836; also Rhode Island news items bearing dates in 1840. Top is lined with *Christian Register* for August 13, 1831.

Yellow, pale green varnish and white on unusual brown background

Oval 18½ x 14, 15" deep   No. 143   Circa 1840

ORIENTAL POPPY

One of the larger boxes covered with wallpaper design incorporating poppy and other flowers. Newspapers date in 1837, 1841 and one from Troy, New York dates in 1842.

Red, white and green varnish on blue background

Oval 20 x 15½, 16" deep

No. 32   Circa 1842

PEONY

Peonies and roses are featured on the wallpaper covering this box. Newspapers lining the box seem to be from New Hampshire and Vermont and show advertisements dating in the year 1839.

Pink, white and green varnish on blue background

Oval 10 x 8, 5" deep   No. 121   Circa 1839

Pink, white and green varnish on
yellow background

Oval 20 x 15, 16″ deep

No. 88   Circa 1844

PINEAPPLE

One of the most charming of the wallpapers covering the Hannah Davis boxes is this pineapple design. It has been reproduced by Jones & Erwin of New York City and entitled: "Portsmouth Pineapple—a documented design with a handsome representation of the exotic fruit which became a symbol of hospitality in the 18th century." New Hampshire newspapers with advertisements dating 1842 and 1844 line the box.

BLACK-EYED SUSAN

The wallpaper covering this box is much faded. A copy of *Northern Gem* lines the interior and advertisements date in 1836 and mention New Hampshire.

Indian red, black and green varnish on grey-blue background

Oval 9½ x 7½, 6″ deep   No. 5   Circa 1836

FANTASY FOLIAGE

Box is covered with wallpaper featuring a variety of stylized foliage and floral forms. The tag pasted on the top is a shipping tag of the Adams Express Company of Worcester, Massachusetts. New Hampshire newspapers lining the box date from 1842 and 1841.

Pink, white and green varnish on blue background

Oval, 12 x 9, 8½″ deep   No. 38   Circa 1842

NAPOLEON AND L'AIGLON

(Eaglet)

Wallpaper printed with vignette of Napoleon holding his son in his arms. The design has been carefully centered on the box and appears on both sides and also on the top. It is framed with chalky scrolls. The newspapers lining the box appear to be from the vicinity of Keene, New Hampshire and show ads dating July 15, August 26 and July 23 of 1829. Bottom of box has pasted December 1797 newspaper.

Pink, white and green varnish on blue background

Oval 14½ x 13, 13″ deep   No. 153   Circa 1829

DUCK SHOOTING

Wallpaper-covered with design of duck hunter with gun in boat holding aloft duck and companion rowing boat framed in chalky white scrolls. Interior newspapers include *New England Galaxy* for May 23 and April 25, 1823. On bottom a late 18th century newspaper.

Red, white and green varnish on blue background

Oval 20 x 15, 16″ deep   No. 124   Circa 1825

TOAST TO THE LADIES

Covered with wallpaper; design repeats two and a half times. Lined with religious newspapers—*Congregational Journal*, advertisements dated 1854 and 1855; *Oberlin Evangelist* with report of missionaries dated 1848; and on bottom of box *Baptist Register* for September 5, 1839.

Pink, white and amber varnish on grey background

Oval 16½ x 13, 14″ deep   No. 140

Circa 1855

THE CONVERSATION

Design repeats twice on sides of box and again on cover. Man dressed in doublet and plumed hat is gesticulating and conversing with Empire-gowned young lady who fondles what appears to be a large-sized dog. In the background sails of a ship are visible. Curving chalky white foliage branches frame the designs and fill in the intermediate spaces. Box is lined with New Hampshire newspapers dating 1844 and 1845.

Pink, white and bright green varnish on blue background

Oval, 15½ x 13, 13½" deep   No. 170   Circa 1845

E PLURIBUS UNUM

An all-over repeating pattern featuring spread eagles and trophies of war, swords, cannons, cannon balls, etc., arranged in clusters has been used to cover this bandbox. Eagle is framed with flowering rose branches and ribbon draped across his breast is printed with U.S. motto *E Pluribus Unum*.

Papers lining the box include *The Register*, Concord, New Hampshire, July 5 and 26, 1832; *The Evangelist* dated January 6, 1832 and on the bottom is a copy of the *Temperance Herald* of Concord, New Hampshire showing dates in October 1834.

Red, white and green varnish on blue background

Oval, 18 x 14, 13½" deep   No. 166   Circa 1834

Hannah Davis and Her Tradecards

Pasted inside the covers of all Hannah Davis wooden bandboxes are small paper tradecards. The borders, sizes, text and type faces vary on these cards. Date given under each tradecard is the year of the latest newspaper lining the box.

*1855

1825

1829

1844

1842

Hannah Davis,

BANDBOX MAKER

1784–1863

1842

1840

1832

1834

1836

* Through the courtesy of Mr. George B. Farnham, President of the Jaffrey Center Village Improvement Society the discrepancy in the Jaffrey-East Jaffrey address of Hannah Davis has been explained. "At the time of Hannah Davis, there was a distinction in post office addresses—the end of the town where Hannah lived being designated as East Jaffrey (post office distinction only) and the residential end of the town being called Jaffrey. It has now been changed to make the east end of the town Jaffrey and the other portion of the town Jaffrey Center. However, for all purposes it was and still is correct to call it Jaffrey." Photo of Miss Davis has been copied from an ambrotype loaned to the museum, courtesy of Mr. Farnham.

HAT BOXES FOR MEN

The Tall or High Hat

The tall hat of silk or polished beaver appeared about 1803 but took some while to become established as a man's fashion. At first this type of head-covering was worn by the post boys who delivered the mail or as a hunting hat by sportsmen. It was also affected by postillions—those men who, mounted on saddles, rode the left hand horse of a pair and directed or drove the vehicle or carriage from this position rather than from a seat on the carriage itself. In order to adjust the tall hat to each individual's head size, the inner band was threaded with a string which could be drawn tightly and tied in a bow, thus securing the hat to the head of the wearer. Even today, sewed to the leather sweatband of a man's hat one can see the vestigial remains of this once functional device in the small, flat woven-ribbon bow.

Styles in men's hats changed almost as frequently as those of women. Sometimes a down-curled brim was the vogue; in other years the towering crown and flat brim were the fashion. Heights in crowns of the tall hats varied from year to year and the measurement of that distance indicated the name of the particular model. "John Bull" measured 5¾" high; the "stovepipe," 7"; "chimney pot," 7½", and the "kite-high dandy," affected only by the fops rose to the towering height of 7¾".

In order to facilitate storage of great numbers of these tall hats checked in the cloak-room during the performance by theatre-goers and opera lovers, the folding opera hat was developed. This could be made up in wool felt, silk or fur felt. It was patented in England by G. Lloyd in 1834 and improved by J. T. Tyler in 1849. Mr. Gibus received a French patent in 1844 and the hat itself came to be known as a "gibus" by many. The "crush" opera hat folded flat under the arm and the "cocked" had a brim which tilted up against the side crown.

High-hat-shaped pasteboard box covered with machine-printed wallpaper in a double border design of checks and "cloud" or "shockwave" patterns; blue, red and white on pale gray background

15 x 12, 9" deep   No. 111
Third Quarter 19th century

High-hat-shaped pasteboard box covered with machine-printed scroll, floral spray and strap-work design wallpaper in green, red and gray on a white background. Top of box lined with uncut printed sheets of the Bible. When acquired the box held an imported French beaver hat "Spring Style 1871" which had been purchased from a Burlington, Vermont men's clothing store.

15 x 12½, 9″ deep   No. 51   Third quarter 19th century

Slim cardboard box covered with dark blue paper, orange border, and lined with blue paper striped in gray. Inside the box is the silk snap crown collapsible opera hat for which it was made. On the underside of hat brim is sterling silver monogram of donor's husband.

Gift of Mme. Albert Brin, Paris France.

12 x 10, 2″ deep   No. 73   Last quarter 19th century

The "Beever" Hat

Many of us have lost sight of the significance of the fur trade in the early history of our country. Indirectly the quest for beaver was an important element in the colonization and settlement of the far western portions of both the United States and Canada.

Beaver pelts were needed by European hat-makers in the 17th century, for both men and women wore the sweeping, wide-brimmed hat made of fur felt. Rabbit fur or the south European castor beaver could be used to make the felt for these hats, but the fine quality fur felt was fabricated from the northern beaver. The best grade pelts, thick and heavy, were taken from animals during the winter and quite naturally the harder the winter, the thicker the fur coat. Consequently Russia was the chief European source of furs until the New World began to send home its pelts.

Russia alone also had the knowledge of a fur dressing technique which permitted the outer or tenacious guard hairs to be combed from the pelt without tearing or otherwise damaging the skin or parchment. These stiff, straight guard hairs stubbornly refused to mat up into felt and so had to be removed before the hatter could get to the thick beaver wool, "duvet" or down—that mass of barbed fur close to the skin which was the portion needed for his product. The prongs or barbs on these particular fur fibers, under heat and friction, interlocked and consolidated into the compact, compressed fabric known as "felt."

The sun-dried pelt or "castor sec" (dried beaver) from the New England colonies and Dutch settlements in New York was in little demand by

Pasteboard box covered with thin blue paper stamped with woodblock top hat in black in two places. When acquired, the box contained a black beaver hat made by Geo. Jepherson of 27 Westminster, Providence, Rhode Island. George Jepherson (Jefferson) first appears in the business directories at 13 Westminster Street in 1860–61. From 1862 through 1881 he is indexed at 27 Westminster Street and the following year, only his home address is given.

13 X 11, 9" deep   No. 52

Probably mid-19th century

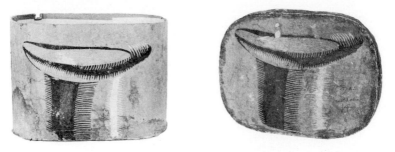

Oval pasteboard box covered with thin blue paper stamped with wood block design of top hat in black with touches of white and red. This hat box belonged to Stephen Wright of Ludlow, Vermont, according to a manuscript note in top of this box.

12½ x 10, 9½" deep   No. 125   Probably mid-19th century

---

the European hatter. In the pelt, castor sec could be used for fur trimmings, garments or bed covers, but for fur felt the skins had to be transported to Russia for processing. It was the "castor gras" (coat beaver, literally oily or fat beaver) which was the real prize to the hat-maker. Castor gras was obtainable from but one source, and that was from an Indian who had worn the skins wrapped about his body for a season. In the process the protruding guard hairs would have broken off and the skins would have become thoroughly greasy from the oils of the Indian's body. This beaver made the glossiest of fur felt hats and the supple skin remaining after the down had been shaved from the parchment could be fashioned into wonderfully soft slippers or other luxury leather goods.

With the hope of breaking the Russian monopoly, both on pelts and on fur dressing, thus freeing up England's economy, a number of courtiers at the court of Charles II organized in 1668 the "Hudson's Bay Company." The resultant expedition established a fort at the foot of James Bay and the "Gentlemen Adventurers Trading Into Hudson's Bay" received their charter, a trading monopoly with the northern Canadian Indians (who customarily wore their furs in such a way as to impart the maximum of oil to the pelt) and practically sovereign rights in the region drained by rivers flowing into Hudson Bay.

France likewise claimed this territory (her representatives complained that the Iroquois with whom they traded had not the specific knack of greasing up their beaver). Constant warfare went on between the two nations in America even after they had made peace in Europe. Ultimately the whole of Hudson Bay was recognized as British territory.

Hudson's Bay Company policy did not encourage exploration and this led to competition from a rival concern. Finally in 1821 the ruinous and bloody dispute was brought to an end by the amalgamation of the com-

Pasteboard box lined with white paper and covered with thin blue paper. The hat inside the box was made by Greenough, Cook & Co. of 50 Congress Street, Boston, Massachusetts and was worn by Albert Francis Davis of Pittsford, Vermont on his 21st birthday—March 6, 1853. Greenough, Cook & Co. were listed at the 50 Congress Street address from 1852 through 1857. In 1858 only James Greenough is listed at this address and the following year, the company no longer appears in the Boston business directories.

14 X 11, 9″ deep   No. 141   Circa 1853

Gift of Mr. Robert V. N. Davis, Rutland, Vermont

---

panies. Now the British-held concern had virtually absolute rule over a vast territory extending from the Atlantic to the Pacific. Even a portion of United States territory was subject to Hudson's Bay Company rule.

In the meantime, Thomas Jefferson had become president of the United States. He had long sensed the need of an expedition to safeguard the rights of the United States to its vast unexplored and uncharted western territory. He discussed the feasibility of such an excursion with his private secretary, Capt. Meriwether Lewis. Congress approved the plan in 1803, the same year the Louisiana purchase became an accomplished fact. After the acquisition of this great tract of land it was apparent that a survey of this immense portion of our country was needed more than ever. Accompanied by William Clark as his associate, Lewis set off to search out a land route to the Pacific and to gather information about the Indians and other data relating to the far west. The first formal report of the excursion appeared in President Jefferson's message of 1806. The Lewis and Clark Expedition was a well-planned and well-executed journey and the importance to the early history of our country of its documentation, maps and charts has never been underrated.

It has been said that beaver was the coin in which the New World paid its debts to the Old. To a degree, we in the New World also have a considerable stake in that form of currency. The quest of the beaver pelt was the link between the discovery and settlement of our West.

Larkin & Packer Hat Box

The labels on this box demonstrate the wide assortment of decorative and fancy type face styles in vogue about the middle of the 19th century. Each of the lines in the tradecard affixed to the box here illustrated shows a different size and style of type. The whole is surrounded with a border composed of ornate printer's "flowers." These elaborate designs used to embellish and frame printed matter are almost as old as movable type. Just 30 years after Gutenberg's invention of the movable type press, two Italian printers designed the movable ornaments and named them "Fleurons" or flowers. Fellow printers were indignant when "Arte de ben Morire," the first book ever to contain flower decorations and borders was published in 1478. Contemporary craftsmen who had formerly added the decorative devices by hand predicted that this infamous commercialization of book decor would lead to the complete decay of the art of book printing and decoration.

Styles in flowers varied from year to year and modes in type faces changed frequently too. The type faces of this era fell into three basic groups. First there was the three-dimensional letter whose depth or relief was made to vary with the strength and blackness of its shadow. The word "Hatters" and "Philadelphia" to a lesser degree demonstrate this.

The second group was the letter which assumed a new form or outline, varying from a simple to a more elaborately embroidered character. An illustration of this complication of characters can be seen in the "Larkin & Packer/ Plain and Fashionable/ Hat and Cap Manufactory." The letters in

13½ x 12, 10″ deep

No. 100   Circa 1855

the last line have been squeezed into a perpendicular form and in order to ornament them, the hairline serifs have been twisted and curled into scrolled volutes.

The third form was letters designed into a background, ribbon or network arrangement.

It has been said the full flowering of the mid-19th century flamboyant advertising style was in no small measure due to the unrestrained outpourings of our type foundries. Certainly the offerings seemed to flow in endless succession and in retrospect, the hundreds of ornamental type faces beggar description.

Research through the Free Library of Philadelphia has failed to establish a definite date for the firm of Larkin and Packer—in fact directories do not list Larkin at all. Two Packers were listed in 1845—one a boxmaker and one a hatter. However, their addresses are different. Lightfoot & Smedley is not listed as a concern, although separately both names appear in directories around mid-century. Madison House is listed as one of the principal hotels in the 1859 Philadelphia Shopping Guide.

The hat box is covered with brown paper, printed in black. There is a blue border re-inforcing the outside rim of the top.

Leather Hat Boxes

In the closing years of the 19th century, although the youthful or more fashionable men gave up wearing a beard, the older professional men kept that face adornment. The mustache was universally worn up to about 1890, but during the next decade, the "Gilded Age," the clean-shaven face vied in popularity.

Antiquated or modern, adolescent or old man—there was no choice in the proper head covering during these years for formal or ceremonial wear. The black silk or beaver top hat held an unchallenged position as *the* dress hat. Even until fairly recent years, the tall hat was worn to formal wedding receptions, by diplomats and by church-goers on Sunday. Photos of the Easter Parade on Fifth Avenue in New York published in the rotogravure sections of our newspapers prove that some of the more fashion-conscious gentlemen still affect this headgear.

With the revival of coaching during the final quarter of the 19th century

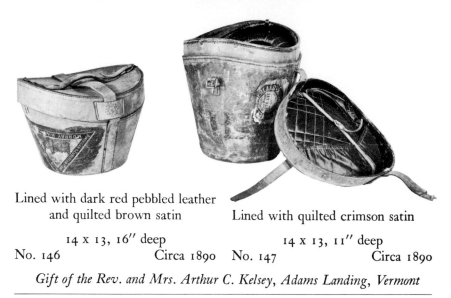

Lined with dark red pebbled leather
and quilted brown satin

Lined with quilted crimson satin

14 x 13, 16″ deep

14 x 13, 11″ deep

No. 146   Circa 1890   No. 147   Circa 1890

Gift of the Rev. and Mrs. Arthur C. Kelsey, Adams Landing, Vermont

the grey or beige tall hat became the suitable head covering for the "whips" who drove the four-in-hand teams harnessed to their park drags and road coaches. At the races and at coaching meets, the grey topper was de rigeur. To the new social set who considered European jaunts a part of their yearly activities, the top hat was an important accessory. To guard and protect it during the sea journey, the leather hat box came into fashion and enjoyed a great vogue. There are several of these boxes in the museum collection, gay with their pasted express company labels and hotel stickers. "Hotel Netherland, New York, absolutely fire proof"; "New York Transfer Company, Dodds Express"; "Murray Hill Hotel, New York"; "American Express Company Foreign Freight and Baggage Department."

Beautifully padded and fitted out, these brown leather hat boxes were lined with quilted satins, pebbled leathers and shiny striped cottons. Sturdy brass fittings and locks were mounted on the boxes and their straps were sewed on with strong linen saddle stitching. The hats were cradled in a nest of luxury. The most sought-after leather goods were those from abroad—London, Paris and Vienna. One could pick up for himself a leather hat box in any of the European capitals or purchase an imported one at Mark Cross or at one of the other well-known New York firms. The traveller could also acquire splendidly extravagant companion leather shirt cases; cuff and collar boxes; military brushes, manicure sets and razors all nestled in velvet or plush; a hunting kit bag with shoe or boot box; or a set of matched suit cases.

The two leather hat boxes shown here belonged to Mr. J. H. Rutherford, whose summer home was located on Grand Isle, Vermont. According to a sticker pasted on the box, one of them was delivered to him at his Murray Hill, New York address on May 1st in 1895.

Lined with red and white striped cotton

13 x 12, 10" deep   No. 164   Circa 1890

Gift of Mrs. R. H. Trott, Providence, Rhode Island

Hat box above was sold in 1891 by "Johs. Michelsen, Sadelmager & Tapetserer" of Kongensgade 6, Kristiania. Kristiania or Cristiania was the name by which the capital city of Norway was known after it was rebuilt in 1624 by Christian IV following a disastrous fire. In 1925 it resumed its ancient name of Oslo.

Note the round box built into the leather cover. The tall beaver hat inside the box was made by Collins & Fairbanks of 381 Washington Street, in Boston, Massachusetts, who were located at this address from 1889 through 1923. This company is at a new location now in Boston, but is still in business.

There are two hat boxes of this pattern in the museum collection. Both are lined with a coarse blue and white glazed striped cotton.

14 x 12, 11" deep
No. 53 and No. 110   Circa 1890

A Variety of Fashionable Headgear

The men depicted on this hat box model a diversity of hat styles, all dating from the era which has come to be known as the French Consulate or Empire period. This epoch spanned the years 1800 to about 1815 and was noted for its extremes in styles and its contradicting modes. Men wore their hair cut short in a Roman Emperor style with straight prongs of hair brushed over forehead and cheeks; men wore their hair curled in loose ringlets; men wore their natural hair or wigs in a queue style which was sometimes powdered. The American soldier's queue was shortened by regulation to seven inches in 1804 and entirely cut off in 1808.

Extremes and opposites were also found in the headgear affected by the masculine sex during this period. The simple ribbon-banded tall hat was the usual headgear and depicted on this hat box are three versions of this hat. One shows the tapering crown later worn by the postillion coachman. The light colored beaver tall hat here worn by the gentleman carrying the umbrella was particularly favored for daytime wear by the English. The stove-pipe shaped black beaver is just visible at the edge of the hat box. The bicorne or Wellington was worn by the military of all countries during this era. The montero cap with visor and earflaps was a very new fashion introduced by military officers, but adopted by jockeys, youngsters and coachmen. It eventually became the correct sports headcovering for the well-dressed man, made up in wool to match his coat. The child wears a type of Glengarry or masculine Scotch bonnet and the hat the lady wears is a capote or poke bonnet.

The word "Fashionable" appears at the top of this box and one can find the words "Gloves, Hats, Caps, Canes, Umbrella and Cases" in the legend at the bottom of the box. The design repeats on the opposite side of the box and again on the cover.

Gift of
Mrs. Katharine Prentis Murphy
New York

Pasteboard box lined with white paper. Covered with wallpaper in red, white and black on yellow background.

Oval 11 x 9, 9" deep
No. 26
Circa 1815

"Hats and Caps"

Several of the pasteboard hat boxes at the Shelburne Museum display block-printed designs featuring men's hats and caps, umbrellas and gloves precisely arranged in cartouches or enclosed in divided panels. These hat boxes date about 1835.

Oval 12 x 9, 9" deep   No. 97 and No. 104   Circa 1835

Illustrated here is a hat box design which is found in two differing color combinations. One of the boxes is printed in black, Indian red, buff and yellow on a blue background and its twin shows a duplicate design in black, Indian red and blue on a bright yellow background. Both boxes feature a large top hat printed in black with a small oval containing an umbrella superimposed on the brim. Below this oval and placed within the crown is another hat. Arranged in the free space around the crown are two diminutive caps, two small-scale top hats and two umbrellas. This entire motif is confined within an octagonal cartouche which appears twice on the box. Side spaces are filled in with polka dots and the cartouche repeats again as a cover subject.

A somewhat similar arrangement of five hats, four umbrellas and eight caps has been block-printed to make the cover design for the hat box appearing on page 40.

Black printed on pale green with blue dots
12 x 9"   Top to Box No. 49

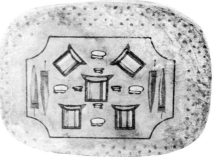

John C. & Charles Cook Hat Box

Reproduced on both sides and on the cover of this trade box is a design featuring two crossed umbrellas with intermediate spaces enclosing a pair

of gloves, a visored cap and a beaver top hat. The word "CAPS" is contained within two bars of black on the side of the box and opposite this division is the word "HATS," also enclosed by two bars. Orange and black are block-printed on a yellow field to make the design. Cover has been re-inforced with a strip of unmatched wallpaper.

Pasted inside the cover of this box is one of the more descriptive tradecards such as are occasionally found inside the boxes. The "chimney board prints" mentioned in the advertisement were panels of wallpaper, usually with landscape scenes,

11 x 9, 9″ deep   No. 92   Circa 1835

which fitted in the space above the fireplace. The "borders" could be used alone or with companion wallpapers such as we use today.

Boston business directories list "John C. and Charles Cook, paperhangings" at 220 Washington Street from 1831 through 1836. Only Charles is listed from 1837 through 1841. The name of Charles Edward Cook, paperhangings is registered at this address from 1842 through 1866. After that date the firm no longer appears in the business directories. See page 130 for another hat box made by the Cooks.

JOHN C. & CHARLES COOK,
IMPORTERS AND MANUFACTURERS OF
PAPER HANGINGS,
BORDERS AND CHIMNEY BOARD PRINTS.

ALSO MANUFACTURE
HAT and BONNET BOXES by the DOZEN or HUNDRED,
AT REDUCED PRICES.

STORE 220 WASHINGTON STREET,
BOSTON.

U. S. Military Head Dress

Charles Willson Peale's first portrait of George Washington, painted 1772 shows the Colonel in uniform, orders for the march thrust into his pocket, rifle at his back, sword at his side and a small, black tricorne with gilt button-type cockade perched squarely on his head. In the so-called "Valley Forge portrait" painted 8 years later, Washington is pictured wearing a post-Revolutionary style tricorne with a gray-white ribbon cockade tied with black cord. Styles had indeed changed, but hatters, according to advertisements published in contemporary newspapers, volunteered to "alter and cock hats in the newest and most approved taste" or to "lace, dress and cock hats in the best manner" if the "gentlemen of the Navy and Army" did not wish to purchase one of the newer "neat cocked beaver hats" they were offering for sale. Nicholas Low of New York in 1785 advertised that any customer could have his hat "cocked, brushed, or dressed up, at any time, at the retail store, gratis."

The bicorne was adopted in the 1790's by military and naval officers, both in this country and abroad. Napoleon's hat, a small version of the Swiss military hat, was a bicorne, and the cocked bicorne affected by the Duke of Wellington, later came to be known by his name and was referred to as a "Wellington." The chapeau was also a cocked hat, but had the advantage of folding flat when not in use. As it was folded and carried under the arm as often as it adorned the wearer's head, it was also referred to as a "chapeau bras."

The earliest known military uniform prints of American manufacture were engraved in Philadelphia to illustrate a Military Manual of 1823. Although eleven plates from this series depicting Pennsylvania militia have been traced, unfortunately no copy of the text seems to have survived. The *United States Military Magazine* between March 1839 and June of 1842 featured a series of uniform plates by Col. William M. Huddy and Peter S. Duval which today are deemed to have no peer in the history of American graphic art for the full-flavored representation of this important aspect of the American scene. The prints are hand-colored facsimiles of the uniform plates "representing the Volunteers of the United States of America together with the Army and Navy" and include the explanatory text as published in the *U.S. Military Magazine*.

There are three versions of the cocked hat or chapeau illustrated in these Huddy & Duval prints. One of them describes and depicts the U.S. Marine Corps hat which was "to be made as a cocked hat and to admit of being closed like a chapeau." The plate picturing Major General Winfield Scott shows him mounted on a grey horse and holding aloft in his right hand a cocked hat with a magnificent cascade of golden cock feathers. Plate No. 13

which was issued August 1840 portrays a "Lieutenant, U.S. Navy." Accompanying text gives the Naval General Order decreeing that "all officers, excepting Chaplains, Schoolmasters, Clerks, Boatswains, Gunners, Carpenters and Sailmakers, are to wear, in full dress, cocked hats bound with black riband, to show one inch and a half on each side, with gold tassels formed with five gold and five blue bullions each, a black silk cockade, with a loop formed with gold lace, and a small Navy button. Captains and Masters Commandant only, to wear when in full dress, gold laced hats, with six bullion loops, the two inner ones to be twisted together."

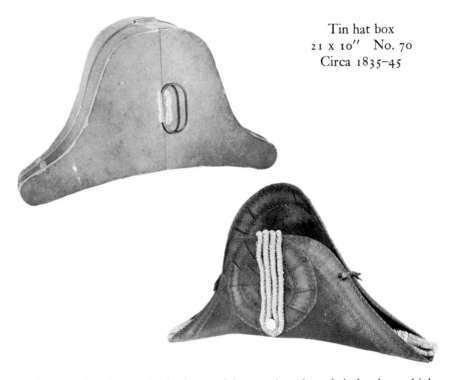

Tin hat box
21 x 10''   No. 70
Circa 1835–45

In the collection at the Shelburne Museum is a shaped tin hat box which contains a cocked hat such as is described above. This beaver hat was purchased in Norfolk, Virginia, from Stevens & Butt of 5 Market Square and the five gold bullions and black silk cockade demonstrate that it was the property of a naval lieutenant. The small Navy button shows the American eagle perched on an anchor which points straight down. Thus the position and direction of the anchor on this button establish the hat as being of the 1835–45 period.

Wallpaper-covered pasteboard box.
White, pink, yellow and green on
ombre field shading from yellow
through green to deep blue

16½ x 8½, 9″ deep
No. 22   Circa 1830–35

A crescent-shaped hat box, covered with fine French hand-blocked wallpaper, once belonged, according to a manuscript notation in the cover, to
George Jones of Chester. The chapeau it contains is of the period 1830–35,
somewhat on the Napoleonic style, but definitely American and earlier
that the above described bicorne. Waverly P. Lewis, collector and author
of articles on U.S. military items, has a similar chapeau with the same style
of gilt cord and satin rosette. It was also found in a wallpaper-covered
shaped box. Newspapers lined this box and in one of them was an item with
a date of 1831.

Block-printed in pink, white and black on yellow background

14¾ x 9″   Panel No. 40   Circa 1830

"Foxing Beaver Toppers"

When this small framed wallpaper fragment was acquired, there was a pencilled notation on the back with the above title and a comment that this was an early 19th century wallpaper or hat box cover. The scene depicted on the panel illustrates two of the operations in the making of fur felt hats.

As early as 1662, the Colonial government of Virginia offered a premium of ten pounds of tobacco (the currency of that time) for every good hat made in the colony of either wool or fur. Ten years later Massachusetts hatters petitioned the General Court for the exclusive privilege of making hats in the colony, but were turned down. By the year 1731, over 10,000 beaver hats were produced in New England and New York. Danbury, Connecticut "Danbury Crowns Them All," even to this day a great hat-making center, had in 1808 more than fifty hat manufacturing concerns, each employing from three to five workmen. For many years, each community had its own hat manufactory, just as each had its own blacksmith and shoemaker. However, the hatters seemed to gravitate toward Danbury, and it came to be known as the Hat City.

Up until fairly recent times, head coverings were customarily worn indoors as well as outdoors by both men and women. Prior to the 15th century both men and women wore close-fitting woolen cloth caps. About 1470 the first felt hat was made in England. The legendary story has it that St. Clement accidentally discovered the process of felting when he placed some rabbits' fur in his shoes to protect his feet during a long journey. At its conclusion he found that the fur had compacted into a homogeneous mass.

Knight's *American Mechanical Dictionary* published in 1877 explains the felting process as follows:

> Fur and wool fibers have barbed surfaces inclined from the root towards their tips. Under the influence of friction and heat these barbs spread out from the main fiber, and like the tendrils of a plant, catch hold of other fibers and cling to them. When a mass of such fibers are disposed in all directions, they readily interlock and consolidate into a compact fabric.

Inventive Yankees worked toward developing machinery to speed up this interlocking and consolidation of fibers from about 1799, but until mid-19th century hat manufacturing was essentially a hand work production from start to finish.

First the fur had to be removed from the rabbit or beaver skin. The guard hairs and the down had to be separated, for it was the under-fur the hatter needed for his product. The loose fur was then ready for the "bower," who with his seven foot bow or stang (which resembled a fiddle or violin bow) placed lightly upon the pile of fur caused the single gut string to vibrate by plucking it with his thumb. The fur would fly up into the air, and with repeated pluckings, the fibers re-arranged themselves into a uniform layer or fleece. Wool fibers were treated in the same manner but with a somewhat larger bow. The bowing operation was the most time-consuming operation in the manufacture of fur felt hats, and it can be seen that when the felting machine was developed to do the work of the bow it revolutioned the manufacture of the felt hat.

Hat-Makers' Battery.

The two layers, one of fur and the other of wool, were placed one over the other and again bowed and the mass was compressed by a wicker frame and afterward by an oilcloth pressed upon it by the hands until the fibers had become thoroughly intertwined and the hat body was brought into a triangular form. This procedure was called "basoning."

According to Knight's *American Mechanical Dictionary:*

> In the next process, called "planking," the body is alternately immersed in a kettle of very dilute sulphuric acid, to which beer grounds or wine-lees are

added, and then worked upon an inclined plane at the side of the kettle until it is shrunk to half its former size and much increased in thickness, the operation being completed by the aid of a rolling pin which smooths and compacts the felt. The body is then dried in a stove, and sized with a brush dipped in shellac dissolved in alcohol, and again dried; any superfluous sizing is removed by dipping in an alkaline solution and scraping. Beaver fur is applied to the exterior by being mixed with fine cotton, and the two are felted, in manner similar to that described, into a thin sheet, which is affixed to the exterior of the body by manipulating it in the boiler and on the plank.

In the wallpaper panel here shown, the workmen are at the hat-makers' battery and are uniting the conical hat-body and the sheet of fur napping, each previously prepared as described above. The water in the kettle was scalding hot and the palms of the workmen's hands were protected by thick pads of leather during this operation.

The hat was then stretched on a wooden block, pressed and coaxed into the proper shape. The brim, puckered and flounced at this point was smoothed with a brim tolliker and the water completely pressed out of the hat. The nap was raised with a wire brush or carding instrument and then sheared to an even length. This required a skillful hand or the nap would lay in furrows.

Dyeing came next. The hats, still stretched on their wooden blocks, were dipped eight times in a solution of logwood, verdigris, oak bark, green copperas or blue vitriol. The hats were allowed to dry out between dippings.

The hat was then stiffened with shellac or glue, which caused it to lose again the shape given to it by blocking. Steam was used to soften the hat again after which it was placed on the finishing block. In our wallpaper panel, the workman at the table on the left is demonstrating this operation.

The brim of the hat was next trimmed to size and after mid-19th century curled to whatever shape was new and fashionable. Prior to that time, most men found the flat brim quite acceptable. Finally the lining was stitched in and the trimmings sewed to the outside. At last the hat was ready to be retailed in one of the hat boxes such as are displayed in the Shelburne Museum collection.

BEASTS, BIRDS, SERPENTS
and THINGS of the SEA

Dromedary and Driver

The design incorporating a camel with his driver was a popular one in the bandbox field and is known in several collections. In the Shelburne Museum collection we have a box featuring this pattern and also a panel. The bandbox shown on page 147 which is totally unrelated to the animal designs uses the camel as a top motif. Our panel is printed in brown and tan on a yellow field, and the bandbox and cover shows the arrangement in white, orange, pink and dark varnish on a blue background.

Travelling exhibitions of rare and curious beasts, the precursors of our circus, were known long before the Revolution in America. Lions, trick horses and performing animals were displayed by itinerant show men and we know that Salem paid to see in 1789, "two camels, male and female, from Arabia," according to a diary kept by one Joseph B. Felt in the *Annals of Salem*.

The Bactrian camel, distinguished by the two humps on its back is from central Asia, but the Arabian camel or dromedary was originally scattered over all southwestern Asia and northern Africa, as well as in India and China. It even roamed the plains of the American

15 x 13"   Top of Box No. 69

---

50 x 11½"   Panel No. 7

Southwest until fairly recent times. San Jacinto's Museum of History in its publication *Camels in Texas* tells the story of one of the most unbelievable and least known of the transportation experiments carried out in America.

In colonial days a few camels had been imported to Tidewater, Virginia, as working beasts, but in 1853, Jefferson Davis, U.S. Secretary of War, undertook the importation of camels from the Mediterranean for servicing military outposts. Between 1856 and 1857, 75 camels were brought by sailing vessel (with a specially rigged camel deck) and landed at Indianola, Texas. Turks, Egyptians, Armenians and Greeks were imported as "camel conductors" and the camel "Khan" was established at Camp Verde, northwest of San Antonio. The first decisive test to demonstrate the camel's wider usefulness was the expedition formed by the government to explore for an all-weather overland route along the 35th parallel through Arizona to California. On the basis of their performance, the Secretary of War recommended the purchase of an additional 1,000 camels.

The "Texas Camel Corps" saw action in the Union forces near the Texas-New Mexico line and Confederate service as well, packing salt from the flats above Brownsville and carrying cotton into Mexico.

California also imported three shipments of camels from mountainous Mongolia, thus assuring their suitability to western terrain.

The hostility of old-time horse men, wagon masters and muleteers, as well as the camel's capacity for frightening horses and mules were factors working against the establishment of the camel as a working beast in America. After the Civil War, the remaining camels were auctioned off to circuses and zoos; a few were purchased by ranchers, and a small number strayed from the original herds. Until fairly recent times, their offspring would occasionally appear in uninhabited places, and it was these last wild survivors wandering in the desert that gave rise to the legend of the phantom camels of the Southwest.

$17\frac{1}{2}$ x 15, 12″ deep   No. 30   Circa 1830

Zoo of Wood Engravings

The newspapers lining this bandbox with its colored wood engravings are from Potsdam, New York and date 1849 and 1850. Many advertisements of local merchants point up the variety of goods to be found in the Potsdam stores. One of the news items in the paper concerns the rates of ship passage to California. A traveller could purchase a ticket for a first class cabin passage in the steamers via Panama for $350 or $400. If he could not afford this rate, steerage with sailor's rations could be had for $200. The trip consumed 40 days, and in addition there was a charge of $20 to $30 to cross from Chagres to Panama (60 miles). Passengers were warned that tickets were sold out a month in advance—the gold rush was on.

Portions of three wood engravings have been printed on the sides of this paper covering the box. The wood engraving of the nest of snakes which decorates the top of the box has been illustrated on page 38.

Only a minute section of the ostrich plume tail can be made out, but the other two circles contain engravings of a porcupine and a hippopotamus.

There are two varieties of the porcupine described in Goodrich's *Pictorial Geography*, a best seller of the 1840 era. One of these is the Canada

10 x 9, 8″ deep   No. 161   Circa 1850

porcupine or urson which is found as far south as Pennsylvania and the western part of New York, but abounds further north and west. Its skin, we are told "is armed with sharp spines or quills covered with sharp prickles, some of which are 12 inches long and capable of being erected at pleasure. When attacked the animal rolls his body into a round form, in which position the prickles are presented in every direction to the enemy." Indians used the quills for ornamenting their moccasins and various other articles of dress. The quills could also be sliced into small rounds, dyed and embroidered onto leather or fabric.

The ubiquitous British explorer, Major Denham, described his encounter in darkest Africa with the hippos as follows:

> It was intended, this evening, to have killed a hippopotamus, an animal which exists in great numbers in the lake, on the border of which we were encamped; but a violent thunderstorm, to our great disappointment, prevented our witnessing so novel a species of sport. The flesh is considered a great delicacy. On the morrow, we had a full opportunity of convincing ourselves, that these uncouth and stupendous animals are very sensibly attracted by musical sounds, even though they should not be of the softest kind; as we passed along the borders of Lake Muggaby, at sunrise, they followed the drums of the different chiefs the whole length of the water, sometimes approaching so close to the shore, that the water they spouted from their mouths, reached the persons who were passing along the banks. I counted 15 at one time, sporting on the surface; and my servant, Columbus, shot one of them in the head, when he gave so loud a roar, as he buried himself in the lake that all the others disappeared in an instant.

Squirrels

There are two squirrel bandboxes in the museum collection, but the positions of the block-printed animals have been reversed. The box below shows what is believed to be the original design, and the inset detail exposes the copied motif. A probable explanation of this transposed motif is that the design was copied or calqued by rubbing the back of a piece of paper with red or black chalk and then turning the paper over and tracing the design onto a block of wood. The block was then carved following the lines of the homemade "carbon copy" sketch. Consequently, when the printing was done, the impression was in a reversed form.

Although the squirrel belongs to the same family as the rat, he seems to have secured for himself the affection and protection of young and old alike.

Jedidiah Morse published the first school geography in America at New Haven, Connecticut in 1784. His text was dedicated to the "Young Masters and Misses" throughout the United States. To his young readers he related a curious belief as regards squirrels:

> Grey squirrels sometimes migrate in considerable numbers. If in their course they meet with a river, each of them takes a shingle, piece of bark, or the like, and carries it to the water; thus equipped they embark, and erect their tails to the gentle breeze which soon wafts them over in safety; but a sudden flow of wind sometimes produces a destructive shipwreck.

Gift of
Mrs. Flora Whiting, New York

Gift of Mr. Richard Gipson and Mr. Roger Wentworth, Arlington, Vermont

Pink, white and green varnish on blue. Pasteboard box lined
with white paper

17 x 13, 11" deep   No. 3, 75, 145   Circa 1835

Giraffe or Camelopard

This bandbox top has been block-printed in pink, white and olive green varnish on a yellow background with a giraffe design.

18½ x 15″

Top No. 20   Circa 1835

Over the years the giraffe, a ruminant mammal living in the country south of the Sahara, has been reduced greatly in numbers because it was destroyed both for its hide and flesh. It is now protected to preserve it from extermination.

In the early years of the 19th century the interior of Africa was investigated by several English explorers. Each of these men left his journal and one of the more interesting accounts was that published by Major Dunham. He furnishes us with the following anecdote:

> On the 11th we arrived at Showy (in Nigritia, or Sudan as the district is known today) after a very tedious march, and losing our way for 3 hours; the woods are indeed, most intricate and difficult and we could get no guides. We saw 5 Giraffes today to my great delight; they were the first I had seen alive, and notwithstanding my fatigue and the heat, Bellal and myself chased them for half an hour; we kept within about 20 yards of them. They have a very extraordinary appearance from their being so low behind, and move awkwardly, dragging, as it were, their hinder legs after them; they are not swift and are unlike any figure of them I ever met with.

The giraffe was considered a suitable gift from one reigning monarch to another and we find records that the Pasha of Egypt gave a giraffe to the King of England in 1827 and in the same year presented a handsome specimen to Charles X of France. It is said that the populace went wild over this animal and within a few days, Paris had named all kinds of costume accessories, both for men and women, "à la giraffe." The coiffure formerly called Apollo's knots, with lacquered loops of hair, was promptly renamed "à la giraffe."

Goodrich's *Pictorial Geography*, published 1840, mentioned that several of the southern giraffes had recently been exhibited in America.

Cows and Ruins

This design is represented in the museum collection on a bandbox cover and also on a panel which is a bandbox steamed open and mounted on a board. Pink, white and dark green varnish on a blue background.

The wallpaper depicts a bucolic scene of three grazing cows pastured on the grounds of a ruined castle. Cattle were first brought to the Western Hemisphere by Columbus on his second voyage.

An early account of the importation of cows to America can be found in Governor Bradford's history of the pilgrim colony. His record—*Of Plimoth Plantation* related in detail the miseries and sufferings encountered by the early colonists, and specifically mentions that in 1624 Mr. Winslow, one of the passengers on *The Mayflower*, had returned from his trip abroad where he had been sent as a representative of the colony, bringing with him "cloathing and other necessaries and three heifers and a bull, the first beginning of any cattle of that kind in the land."

16½ x 13″   Top No. 8

29 x 9″   Panel No. 29   Circa 1835

Penguin, Ocelot And Ostrich

This bandbox covered with block-printed wallpaper in pink, white and olive green varnish on a blue field might well have served as an illustrated text book in the study of natural history. Three exotic creatures are depicted in their natural habitat.

15½ x 11½, 10″ deep

No. 50   Circa 1835

A contemporary geography described the penguin, here shown floating on a cake of ice as a "half bird and half fish. They form long files along the beach like a procession of monks, and sit in great numbers upon the nests, so closely placed together as to form considerable towns, as they are called by the sailors. This bird has merely a sort of finny wings, which it uses as oars in the water, and is wholly unable to fly; it is so stupid and inactive as to suffer itself to be knocked down with a club, and its upright posture and grave air give it a most ludicrous aspect when ashore."

The same geography, Goodrich's *Pictorial Geography*, published 1840, delineated the ostrich as a native of the torrid regions of Africa:

It is generally considered as the largest of birds, but its great size, and the shortness of its wings, deprives it of the power of flying. The weight of this bird may be estimated at 75 to 80 pounds. It inhabits the most solitary and arid deserts, where there are few vegetables and where the rain never comes to refresh the earth. It is said that the ostrich never drinks, but it is of all animals the most voracious, devouring leather, glass, iron, stones or anything that it can get. The savage nations of Africa hunt them not only for their plumage, but for their flesh, which they consider a great dainty.

The detail view of the ostrich shown on the bandbox may exaggerate its size, but the over-stated height of the bird conveys the impression that indeed it would be impracticable if this bird could fly.

In another contemporary publication, the ocelot was pictured and described as being one of the most beautiful of the "cat kind," with its coat described in detail—gray, slightly tinged with pale fawn and covered with longitudinal stripes, broken into patches black at the margins and pale inside with an open space in the center of the ordinary ground color of the fur. This animal, measuring about 3 feet in length and in height about 18 inches "is a native of South America where it frequents the depths of the forest, living upon deer and birds. It seldom attacks man, though instances have occurred of its so doing. When hunted and overtaken, it defends itself with great obstinacy. It is fierce and savage, and less susceptible of domestication than other members of the cat tribe." The Mexican word "thalocelotl," from which it received its name, means "jaguar of the field."

Alpine Rescue

The pasteboard box, lined with white paper, is covered with wallpaper in tan, brown, white, green, blue, red and orange on a gray ground.

Design on this box highlights the rescue of a half-frozen traveller, and his discovery by the dogs sent out in advance of the party. Arabesques and swirls of white enclose this motif and frame floral bouquets above and below the rescue scene.

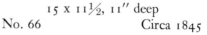

15 x 11½, 11″ deep

No. 66   Circa 1845

Traditionally the largest of domestic dogs, the Saint Bernard dog, was bred from the 17th century by monks for rescuing lost persons in the mountains. Its origin is uncertain, but it is believed that a cross with the Newfoundland dog about 1830 contributed the long hair to the breed, although modern varieties in both the smooth and rough coat are known. Head and shoulders are massive and some of these dogs exceed 200 pounds in weight when full grown. They are intelligent, powerfully built and possess a keen sense of smell.

There are two well-known Alpine passes which have been used since antiquity. One of these is the Great Saint Bernard, located in Valais canton,

Switzerland and Val d'Aosta, Italy. The conquering armies of Charlemagne, Emperor Henry IV, Frederick Barbarossa and Napoleon I all used this pass. Augustinian friars are in charge of the hospice founded there at an altitude of over 8000 feet by St. Bernard of Menthon about 982.

There is another hospice at Little Saint Bernard with its road from Val d'Aosta, Italy to Savoy, France. This too was founded by Saint Bernard of Menthon, the 10th century Savoyard Churchman whose life was spent working among the peoples of the Val d'Aosta. St. Bernard is the patron saint of mountaineers, and his feast day falls on May 28th.

Boa Constrictor
ALSO KNOWN AS
ABOMA OR ANACONDA

"The woods of South America are full of venomous reptiles and serpents. The Boa, or as it is called in the country, the Aboma, is a large amphibious snake about 40 feet in length. . . . It is indifferent to its prey and destroys when hungry any animal that comes within its reach; the negroes consider it excellent food and its fat is converted into oil. It is met with principally in Guiana and the northern parts of Brazil"—Goodrich's *Pictorial Geography*, published 1840. This fearful snake was known as the Anaconda in Asia and although non-poisonous was considered the most terrible of reptiles, in its coils it could crush mammals as large as a deer.

Wood engraving in green, yellow and blue, shows nest of snakes

10 x 9"   Top of box No. 161
          Circa 1850

A print of a boat's crew being attacked by a boa constrictor was published in Smith's *First Book in Geography* which was an introductory geography designed for children, illustrated with 126 engravings and 20 maps. First entered in the Clerk's office in 1846, it proved a very popular text

A Boat's Crew attacked by a Boa Constrictor.

book, and the copy in the Shelburne Museum research library, dated 1856 is from the 29th edition. The little quarto volume was highly recommended by a contemporary teachers' association committee on books as a "simple, comprehensive and useful treatise for beginners . . . with questions judiciously arranged and answers giving the general and important divisions of the globe, with the particular localities of all important places, together with a knowledge of the state of Society, habits and customs of the different races of men."

The design on the wallpaper panel follows the engraving closely, except that the block with which it was printed has been simplified to include only the native with upraised oar.

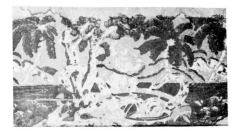

Pink, white and green varnish on blue ground

20 x 12"   Panel No. 39

Circa 1830–35

56 x 10"   Panel No. 6

12½ x 9½, 8″ deep

No. 49   Circa 1835

The Beaver

So, William, you thought you had done vastly well,
    Such a rabbit-hutch maker is clever;
Yet some of the bars are quite split with the nail,
And one of the hinges is ready to fail;
    I think you might learn of the beaver.

How neat is his house, 'tis not clumsy in shape,
    Smoothed over with mud as with plaister:
No cracks let in water, no crevices gape,
No tying together with pack-thread or tape;
    Could you do the same, my young master.

The entrance is under the water, and there
    They go to their chambers and cellars.
You will not go with them, although you might share
Of the stores they've provided, all plenteous and rare;
    But content you to call them fine fellows.

And look at that bank all across the clear stream,
    To keep the sweet waters from sinking;
What mud work, and stone work, and many a beam;
How clever, and wise, and laborious they seem;
    'Tis wonderful well to my thinking.

Ah, could they enjoy it!—but man will one day
    Come hunting, and alter the matter;
He'll make all their dads, aunts and sisters his prey;
Then travel a thousand miles off, far away,
    And sell their soft skins, to the hatter.

This little poem is quoted from:

> *Scenes in America for the Amusement and Instruction of Little Tarry-at-home Travellers*, by the Rev. Isaac Taylor, published Hartford, Conn. in 1825.

On the facing page is one of the more interesting bandboxes in the museum collection. Top of this box is illustrated on page 21, and there are two differing designs on the sides of the box separated by a dotted pattern. A steamboat, see page 127, is printed on the side opposite the beaver here illustrated. Colors are black, blue and green, block-printed on a pale green background.

The beaver wallpaper fragment below is framed as a panel. Beaver, tree and dome-shaped beaver hut are printed in blue on a medium blue background.

Gift of
Mr. Richard Mills and
Mr. Harry S. Newman,
New York

18 x 11″   Panel No. 31
Circa 1835

Horse at Watering Trough

This pasteboard bandbox has been lined with an interesting 1822 issue of the *Eastern Argus*, a semi-weekly journal published in the State of Maine.

The block-printed design in pink, white and bright green varnish on a blue background shows a vignetted scene of mounted farmer watering his horse with two cows in foreground. Between the vignettes a crane with bent neck drinking from a slim-neck bottle is featured.

17½ x 13, 12″ deep

No. 150   Circa 1822

On the front page of this newspaper is an article setting forth amendments to the act regulating trade and intercourse with the Indian Tribes with the hope of preserving peace on the frontier. The amendment, signed by President James Monroe, is dated at Washington May 6, 1822. The facts leading up to this amendment and subsequent acts are of interest to all of us, even today, for they serve to remind us that our treatment of the native Americans has not always been above reproach.

Our problems with the Indians were not even acknowledged as a national responsibility until 1824 when the United States created a Bureau of Indian Affairs. Ironically in its infancy, this bureau was a part of the War Department and not until 1849 did an act of Congress transfer its activities to the United States Department of the Interior. Prior to its establishment, the War Department had jurisdiction over trade with the Indians, their removal to the West, their protection from exploitation and their removal to reservations. Army administration proved unsuccessful, but even after the establishment of the new Bureau, there were continuing Indian wars.

In the Plains area, two types of Indian civilization were found. The sedentary tribes lived in permanent villages of dome-shaped earth lodges and raised corn, squash and beans. The nomads moved about with their goods on dog-drawn travois and eked out their precarious existence by hunting buffalo. At first these Indians roamed about on foot, but after the Spanish at the beginning of the 18th century introduced the horse to the Southwest, their life changed abruptly. Now mounted on horseback and armed with bow and arrow these nomad tribes were constantly on the war-path. The highly mobile tepee served as their home and their food consisted mainly of buffalo meat, fresh during the hunting season and pounded and dried for the lean days out of season. Buffalo hides and deerskins furnished their clothing.

These Indians existed by the system of the "coup" and were perpetually at war with the white man. The coup has been described as a sort of war honor in a complex system of warrior prestige. The coups were earned by acts of bravery, valued according to degree of recklessness. For instance, the coup with the highest count was the defiant act of striking an armed enemy with the bare hand. However, killing, wounding, scalping and horse or gun stealing were all coups of value. These coups were recited at important social functions and a high coup count gave status at feasts, ceremonials and in the tribe. Even after active warfare ceased, young men in order to acquire warrior status in the tribe had to obtain coups by transfer from the older men.

A series of treaties between 1820 and 1845 limited certain areas to the Indians. These lands, known as Indian Territory, were constantly encroached upon by white settlement, and several states were created from territory which had been set aside for the Indians by the Indian Intercourse Act passed in 1834.

Today United States Indians live on some 200 reservations and the population is increasing. When Columbus discovered America, Indians north of Mexico numbered some 900,000. After wars, starvation and epidemics of white men's diseases, by 1870 the population had dwindled to 300,000. Since then it has increased one-third, and in 1945, Indian population stood at 400,000.

A more humane approach to the treatment of these dispossessed Americans has improved their lot and new advances in medicine have restored their health.

Charioteer with Bird-drawn Chariot

This ethereal scene incorporates two huge imaginary birds harnessed to and towing through the clouds a fantastic bandwagon. The chauffeur charioteer poised with no visible means of support on the front of the

Two of these motifs in pink, white and amber varnish on a canary yellow background make up this bandbox.

17 x 13, 12″ deep

No. 149   Circa 1835

vehicle is holding in her hand a trumpet which she is about to raise to her lips. Her companion clutches three lightning bolts or arrows and wears a staff mounted on her head band.

The little temple of love firmly anchored to nothing in the background is surmounted by a small female weathervane figure balanced on one leg. In one of her hands she grasps a wreath and in the other a racket form.

Charioteer with Lion-drawn Chariot

Chariot races have been associated with circuses since earliest times when the Roman circus was a round or elliptical structure with tiers of seats for spectators enclosing the ring space where races, gladiatorial combats and games took place. Although the horse-drawn chariot was not often used in Greek or Roman battle (perhaps because of unfavorable topography) it has always played a prominent part in games and processions, especially as the triumphal car in victory parades.

This bandbox, block-printed in blue, pink, red, white and olive green varnish on blue background, shows the Roman chariot being drawn by a lion. This phenomenon is often depicted in classical architecture as a frieze decoration carved into marble or a mural painted onto walls. How the lion, symbol of royal power and strength since Biblical times, was trained to perform as a work beast is an art which has been lost through the ages.

17 x 14½, 11½" deep   No. 142   Circa 1835

The Hunt

In the New England area during the late 18th and early 19th century, hunting was somewhat restricted, as according to Puritan precepts, sports as mere pastimes were undesirable. In the South where the upper classes still clung to English tradition, sports, including hunting and fishing, were much in favor. Wild fowl shooting, deer hunting, riding after hounds were all important segments of the social life of a Southern Gentleman. George Washington was president not only of the United States, but also of the Virginia Jockey Club and one of the most accomplished riders of his day. He boasted of running a pack of hounds so close that it could be "covered with a blanket." During the Revolution, of necessity he neglected his hunting, but after the war was ended, his friend LaFayette presented him with a pack of swift French hounds, and Washington took up the sport again.

Both in the north and in the south during this period religious news-papers built up and kept alive a prejudice against outdoor sports with their articles and assertions that the pursuit of sports was a prodigal waste of time, un-christian and against the design of all spiritual institutions. When progressive and highly respected men like Benjamin Franklin and Dr. Benjamin Rush spoke up and recommended outdoor recreation, including swimming, as an aid to health, their opinions tended to break down the bias against sports. The really great change of opinion, however, came in the late 1830's when an Englishman, writing under the pen name of "Frank Forester" published his series of essays and books on hunting and fishing. The outdoor sportsman and hunter gradually came to be looked upon as a skilled woodsman, exemplary of the virility and ruggedness of American men.

RUSTIC BRIDGE

Two different designs of bonnet box paper have been mounted side-ways on this box. One of the designs is Castle Garden (see page 166) and the other shows a rustic bridge with mounted horseman, hunter and dogs. This bandbox is one of the largest in the collection—20 x 17, 14″ deep. Printed in pink, yellow, white and green varnish on blue background. Panel measures 29 x 9″ and shows the same design. In this case the bandbox was steamed open and mounted to show complete design.

Box 91, Panel 27   Circa 1830–40

AL FRESCO LUNCH

Two views of this bandbox show the design printed in faded pink, black and gray varnish on bleached yellow background. A servant with cocked hat carries a lunch basket to the hunters who are just completing their morning of sport.

14 x 10½, 10″ deep   No. 151   Circa 1830–40

GAME WARDEN AND POACHER

Wallpaper fragment printed in pink, white and amber varnish on yellow background. Depicted on this panel is the hunter caught with the goods—in this case a rabbit—by the game warden who points to the corpus delicti.

21″ x 11½   Panel No. 43   Circa 1835

38 x 15" Panel No. 20   Circa 1830–40

AMERICAN DEER HUNT

Bandbox steamed open and pasted to two pieces of board make up this panel. White, pink and olive green varnish have been block-printed on a yellow background.

END OF THE HUNT

Wallpaper fragment printed in pink, white and amber varnish on blue background. The hunt is now over and the sportsmen are loading the day's kill into their high-flyer phaeton and preparing for their trip home. One of the hunters holds aloft a rabbit, while his friend stoops to retrieve another hare.

The folding top to this vehicle was of the type known as a "calash." The same principle was applied to women's bonnets during the late 18th century when the mammoth puffed-out hair-dos were in vogue. The silk or satin material of the bonnet was stretched over covered stays in such a way that the entire bonnet could be collapsed when it was not being worn. These bonnets were likewise known as "calashes."

Gift of Mr. J. Watson Webb, Jr., Los Angeles, California

21" x 10½ Panel No. 46   Circa 1830–40

Laisser Courre

One of the greatest pleasures of the Chase is the music of the traditional hunting horns. This bandbox top shows us the "bouton" who is about to sound the "Laisser Courre" after which the equipage will ride off through the forests following the hounds according to centuries-old custom.

Pink, white and green varnish on blue ground

17 x 13" Top No. 9 Circa 1830–40

Stag Hunt

Pasteboard bandbox steamed open and mounted on panel. Covered with block-printed wallpaper in pink, white and green varnish on a blue ground.

The stag hunt is one of the world's oldest sports, and to this day maintains its traditional ritual. In France the ageless pageantry of the Chasse à Courre still flourishes in the forests of Chantilly. Each week during the season the Rallye Pique-Avant, a group of leading French sportsmen, gather at the Chateau de Chantilly in Oise to re-inact the Chase with all its brilliance and splendid array. The stag is roused by an advance party and then the hounds are unleashed under the supervision of the hunt master after the "rapport" or council is held to determine the best hunting area. The dramatic climax occurs when the stag is brought to bay by the hounds, and the "mort" is sounded on the horns.

15 x 11"   Panel No. 15   Circa 1830–40

Wild Bull Hunt

This bandbox is made of pasteboard and is lined with white paper. The cover is missing and the sides are covered with block-printed wallpaper in white, pink and green varnish on blue field.

One side of the box shows the mounted hunter with sharpened lance preparing to lunge at the enraged wild bull who has gored one of the dogs and tossed him into the air. The wild bull or aurocks, we are informed by Goodrich's *Pictorial Geography* published in Massachusetts in 1840 is chiefly to be met with in the extensive forests of Lithuania. The beast is further described as black and of great size, with red and fiery eyes, thick and short horns and a forehead covered with a quantity of curled hair. A modern-day dictionary describes the aurocks as a nearly extinct species of cattle with shaggy coat and mane now found only in Lithuania and the Caucasus, where it is strictly protected by law.

Hunting scenes were popular subject matter for the paper-stainers or wallpaper designers. A contemporary newspaper advertised that a local auctioneer in March of 1825 had for sale elegant paper hangings—among them a tiger hunt, hunting the deer and fishing.

Gift of
Miss Katrina Kipper,
Accord, Mass.

12½ x 11, 10" deep

No. 60

Probably late 18th century

Rhinoceros Hunt

In the first half of the 19th century there was intense interest every-where in the habits and appearance of exotic birds and beasts. Kings and royalty kept private menageries and itinerant animal trainers and showmen roamed the American countryside exhibiting uncommon and incredible animals from foreign lands. In Boston, about 1825, a year-old rhinoceros from Calcutta was exhibited, according to the story set forth in *Book of Quadrupeds:*

> It was six feet in length and three feet four inches in height. The horn had not yet made its appearance, but a large protuberance indicated the place where it was growing. It fed upon hay, potatoes and grain and was very greedy.

This little book pointed out to its juvenile readers that next to the elephant the rhinoceros was the most powerful of animals.

> His upper lip is movable and in this is centered all his dexterity. On his nose is a hard, solid horn which is so placed as to protect not only the neck and head, but the muzzle, the mouth and the face. In 1790 one of these animals was carried to England and was sold for 700 pounds. He was very mild and al-lowed himself to be patted on the back by strangers. . . . His daily allowance of food was 28 pounds of clover, besides an equal allowance of ship bisquit and a great quantity of greens; he drank five pails of water every 24 hours and liked sweet wines and was sometimes indulged with a few bottles.

The wallpaper fragment covering the flattened bandbox making up this panel has been block-printed in red, pink, white and amber varnish on a blue background. The scene captures an exciting moment of action in the course of a rhinoceros hunt. The native hunter in the background is vainly

20 x 13″   Panel No. 41   Circa 1835

trying to attract the attention of an infuriated rhinoceros. The beast has tossed the second native hunter into the air and the mounted sportsman hunter, dressed in a European gentleman's hunting costume is fleeing from the wrath of the enraged brute.

Wolf Attack

About dusk, an immense-sized wolf rushed out of a thick copse a short distance from the pathway, planted himself directly before me in a threatening position and appeared determined to dispute my passage. He was not more than 20 feet from me. My situation was desperate, and as I knew that the least symptom of fear would be the signal for attack, I presented my stick and shouted as loud as my weak voice would permit. He appeared somewhat startled and retreated a few steps, still keeping his piercing eyes firmly fixed on me. I advanced a little, while he commenced howling in a most appalling manner; and supposing his intention was to collect a few of his comrades to assist in making an afternoon repast on my half-famished carcass, I redoubled my cries, until I had almost lost the power of utterance, at the same time calling out various names, thinking I might make it appear I was not alone. An old and a young lynx ran close beside me, but did not stop. The wolf remained about fifteen minutes in the same position; but whether my wild and fearful exclamations deterred any others from joining him, I cannot say. Finding at length my determination not to flinch, and that no assistance was likely to come, he retreated into the wood, and disappeared in the surrounding gloom.

—Ross Cox, *Adventures on the Columbia River*, written about 1832.

The above report of a wolf attack was published in Goodrich's *Book of Quadrupeds for Youth* which ran through many editions and was published in Brattleboro, Vermont. Such attacks were not infrequent in our wild and unsettled country, but it seems unusual to find such a scene block-printed on a wallpaper-covered hat box.

Red, white and amber varnish on green ground

11½ x 49″ Panel No. 16   Circa 1835

Water Spaniel Flushing Ducks

Mr. Samuel G. Goodrich (well-known 19th century author of school text books and other educational publications) collected 200 engravings of animals and published them at Brattleboro, Vermont in 1832 in a children's book entitled *Book of Quadrupeds for Youth, Embracing Descriptions of the Most Interesting and Remarkable Quadrupeds in All Countries with Particular Notices of Those of America*. On page 60 he described the water spaniel and illustrated the text with an engraving.

On the wallpaper covering the bandbox here shown, a marsh scene with water spaniel driving ducks from cover has been block-printed with red, white and yellow varnish on a blue background. The spaniel hiding in the bullrushes close by the earth mound depicted in the wallpaper shows more action than the dog in the engraving, but because of the similarity of the setting and the reversed position of the scene, it may well be that the wallpaper design was adapted from the *Book of Quadrupeds* engraving.

17½ x 15, 12″ deep

No. 134   Circa 1840–45

Bandbox panel steamed open and mounted to show complete design

49 x 11″   Panel No. 18

Parrot

In Oriental countries, parrots served as royal cage birds from the beginning of time and in our written literature, these bright-hued pets are mentioned as one of the preferred personal importations of sailors returning to their homeland. Today the little paroquet (or parakeet) is on the crest of a new wave of popularity. Love birds are the small scale edition of the parrot and the cockatoo and macaw are also members of this large order of birds. Chiefly tropical or sub-tropical, they are to be found in both hemispheres. Colorings are rich and varied and the parrots of South America with their gaudy and showy feathers of green, blue and red are noted for their superb plumage.

Parrots live on fruits and seeds and their hoarse voice can be taught to mimic or imitate the speaking voice of humans, which is probably another reason for their popularity. With good care, parrots may live for as long as a hundred years.

The parrot design appears twice in the museum collection—both representations are on bandbox covers, and both are in poor condition. Over the years, unless protected, all of the bandbox covers have become spotted with water and soiled with accumulations of dust.

Pink, white and green varnish on pale blue field	Pink, white and amber varnish on yellow field
17 x 13½″ Top to box No. 10	20 x 15″ Top to box No. 31
Circa 1835	Circa 1835

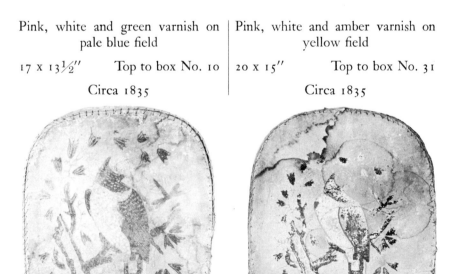

Bird on a Swinging Vine

When found this box had neither a top nor a bottom. It is covered with block-printed wallpaper in blue and white plus olive-green varnish on a yellow background, now faded to white.

In the 1830's there was a great deal of interest evidenced in birds, and they were kept as pets by many young ladies. In the Godey Books all through the 1832 issues they ran a series of sketches with engraved illustrations on a variety of birds. Mrs. Felicia Hemans, an English poetess who regularly contributed to Godey's *Lady Book* wrote an idyl entitled "The Freed Bird" which appeared in B. D. Emerson's *Second Class Reader* "designed for the Use of the Middle Class of Schools in the United States" first published in 1833. The sentiments expressed by the bird in the poem were certainly those of the blue bird pictured on our bandbox!

15 x 11, 9" deep   No. 131   Circa 1835

THE FREED BIRD

Return, return my bird!
I have dressed thy cage with flowers,
'Tis lovely as a violet bank
In the heart of forest bowers.

'I am free, I am free,—I return no more!
The weary time of the cage is o'er!
Through the rolling clouds I can soar on high,
The Sky is around me—the blue bright sky!

'The hills lie beneath me, spread far and clear,
With their glowing heath-flowers and bounding deer,
I see the waves flash on the sunny shore—
I am free, I am free,—I return no more!'

Alas, alas, my bird!
Why seek'st thou to be free?
Wert thou not blest in thy little bower,
When thy song breathed nought but glee!

'Did my song of summer breathe nought but glee?
Did the voice of the captive seem sweet to thee?
Oh! hadst thou known its deep meaning well,
It had tales of a burning heart to tell.

'From a dream of the forest that music sprang,
Through its notes the peal of a torrent rang;
And its dying fall, when it soothed thee best,
Sighed for wild flowers and a leafy nest. . . .
Farewell! With my song through the clouds I soar,
I pierce the blue skies—I am earth's no more!'

Eagle with Prey

The design printed on the bandboxes here illustrated was a popular one and appears in several versions in the museum collection, sometimes covering the sides of the box; at other times pasted on the box top.

Pinky orange, yellow and green varnish on ombre background, (pink to yellow) matching top

18 x 14, 12″ deep   No. 87   Circa 1835

Pink, white and tan varnish on faded yellow background, top printed with Erie Canal scene (see page 134)

15 x 11, 10″ deep   No. 62   Circa 1835

Grey, white and brown varnish on pale pink field

55½ x 13″   Panel No. 8   Circa 1835

Dr. Benjamin Franklin, one of the members of the original three-man committee chosen to prepare a device for a seal of the United States of America was not happy with the eventual designation of the bald eagle as the representative of our country.

> He is a bird of bad moral character; he does not get his living honestly; you may have seen him perched on some dead tree, where, too lazy to fish for himself, he watches the labor of the fishing hawk; and when that diligent bird has at length taken a fish, and is bearing it to his nest for the support of his mate and young ones, the bald eagle pursues him and takes it from him. With all this injustice, he is never in good case; but like those among men who live by sharping and robbing, he is generally poor, and often very lousy. . . . In truth, the turkey is in comparison a much more respectable bird, and withal a true native of America.

A story in B. D. Emerson's *Third-Class Reader* published about 1834 drew a moral from Lesson Twelve—"The Eagle that made a Mistake" which also had to do with the predatory habits of the eagle.

> One day an eagle who was soaring high in the air thought he saw a fine fat rabbit, sleeping comfortably on a bank in the sun. "Ah, Hah! my fine fellow," says he, "I will spoil your nap very quickly. You shall make me a nice dinner." So down he pounced upon the sleeping animal, stuck his sharp claws in his back and bore him off into the air. He had not flown far, however, before he found that he had made a very great mistake, for the creature he had taken for a rabbit, turned out to be a ravenous wild cat. The wild cat, you may well suppose was a good deal astonished at finding himself pinched so unmercifully in the back, and flying off through the air over the hills and tree tops, six times as fast as a stage-coach or steamboat. So he laid hold of the eagle's throat with might and main and soon made him repent of his bargain. Down they both came to the ground; and the eagle was killed while the wild cat escaped with a trifling wound.
> I have known a great many bad boys who fared almost as badly as the eagle. They were fond of doing mischief to other people, but they always did more injury to themselves than to any one else.

Eagles and Aerie

These bandbox tops show a brood of fledgling eagles perched in a tree watching the parent eagle, who hovers over the now-empty nest. This treatment of the eagle family seems to have been reserved as a bandbox cover motif and appears twice in differing color combinations in the museum collection.

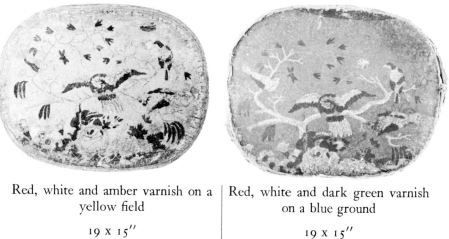

Red, white and amber varnish on a yellow field	Red, white and dark green varnish on a blue ground
19 x 15″	19 x 15″
Top No. 81 Circa 1835	Top No. 5 Circa 1835

Americans dearly loved their eagle, both as a decorative device and as a symbol of their strength and might in the early years of the 19th century. This exaggerated usage of the American emblem, both in decoration and speech, did not go unnoticed or unmarked by visitors to our land. Capt. Marryat, an Englishman who visited our country in the 1830's mentioned in his *Diary in America:*

> It is astonishing how little work they (the congressmen) get through in a session at Washington. This is owing to every member thinking himself obliged to make two or three speeches, not for the good of the nations, but for the benefit of his constituents. These speeches are printed and sent to them, to prove that their member makes some noise in the house. The subject upon which he speaks is of little consequence, compared to the sentiments expressed. It must be full of eagles, star-spangled banners, sovereign people, claptrap, flattery and humbug.

Rainbow Pennants
and
Lithographed Eagle

Heavy pine bottom and top are used on this all wood box covered with gesso, painted with white paint and decorated with streamers or pennants of blue, green, yellow and orange. Open wreath frames the lithographed eagle tinted in color and banner above his head carries the motto *E Pluribus Unum.*

Round, 13″ diameter, 10½″ deep   No. 173   Mid-19th century

Eagle On Urn

Fragment of bandbox paper printed in pink, white and amber varnish on yellow background. Spread eagle with sprig of olive in his beak is poised on graceful urn with olive wreath handles.

12½ x 11″
Panel No. 47
Circa 1830

Putnam and Roff Eagle

Threaded through his beak and looped through the talons of this spread eagle are ribbons advertising PUTNAM AND ROFF PAPER HANGINGS and BAND BOX MANUFAC[r]. Olive branch and laurel spray balance empty spaces on either side of trunk which is stamped with HARTFORD, CON. address of this early 19th century wall paper manufacturer. Cooper Union Museum in New York has a complete bandbox showing this design. Our fragment is printed in black, brown, white and green varnish on pale blue background.

20 X 12″

Panel No. 48

Circa 1823

Swimming Ducks

This scene of two ducks swimming appears twice in the museum collection and both the box tops which they decorate are here reproduced so that a comparison can be made as to the variety that could be gained by the way the colors were placed within the outlines. The small church in the background is surmounted by a steeple and aquatic plants and water lilies fill in the foreground.

Pink, white and amber varnish on blue background	Pink, blue and amber varnish on yellow background
17 x 12½"	17½ x14"
Top No. 25 Circa 1840	Top No. 21 Circa 1840

Cover at left was made by S. M. Hurlbert whose name appears at 25 Court Street with the addition of his business—paper hangings—for the first time in the 1833 Boston business directory. It is listed in the same way through the 1845 directory. In 1846 it became "Hurlbert & Gregory (S. H.) paper hangings, 25 Court." The company does not appear in directories after that date.

Paper is made from a ground linen, cotton or wood pulp; pasteboard is made by compressing this pulp. On the inside cover of this box the small chewed or crushed, ground-up pieces of wood from which the pasteboard was made are visible as darker spots.

Pasteboard; covered with block-printed wallpaper in pink and tan with
amber colored varnish on pale yellow field

16½ x 11, 11″ deep   No. 1   Circa 1845

Pair of Ruffed Grouse

The grouse design appears on the top of one of the boxes in the museum
collection and also on the sides of a box made by Mark Worthley, of
Boston. Worthley, fancy boxes, is listed at 119 Washington from 1839

through 1845 and in 1846 his address changes in Boston business directories to 185 Washington Street.
The company is not listed after that
year. Apparently his company was
located at 104 for only a short while
prior to 1846.

The top of this Worthley box shows a confronted rooster or cock
and a hen. In the background there is a church and working in the field a
farmer is plowing his land.

Mr. Goodrich, when he published his *Pictorial Geography* in 1840 included more than 1,000 engravings, a phenomenal number of illustrations

Pink, white and amber varnish on
yellow. 17 x 13½″. This oval top
has been mounted on a rectangular
board which measures 19 x 15″.
Top No. 4   Circa 1845

at that time. Several varieties of Grouse were included—among them the Pinnated Grouse or Heath Hen, the Sharp-tailed Grouse, Spotted Grouse, Dusky Grouse and the Ruffed Grouse. He pointed out that this latter variety (Tetrao umbellus) is known as Partridge in New England and as Pheasant in the south.

> It always prefers the woods, is seldom or never found in open plains, but loves the pine-sheltered declivities of mountains, near streams of water. Its manners are solitary; they are seldom found in coveys of more than four or five together, and more usually in pairs or singly. They leave the woods early in the morning and seek the path or road to pick up gravel. They generally move along with great stateliness, their broad fan-like tails spread out. The drumming, as it is called of the pheasant, is another singularity of the species. This is performed by the male alone, and is produced in the following manner. The bird standing on an old prostrate log, lowers his wings, erects his tail, contracts his throat, elevates the two feathers on his neck, and inflates his whole body, somewhat in the manner of a turkey cock, strutting and wheeling about with great stateliness. After a few manoeuvres of this kind, he begins to strike with his stiffened wings in short and quick strokes, which at first are low and distinct, but gradually increase in rapidity till they run into each other. This is most common in the morning and evening, and may be heard half a mile off, by which means the sportsman is led to the place of his retreat.

Pineapple and Swans

In 1770 when the blond fourteen-year-old Antonio (later to be known as Marie Antoinette) left her home in Austria to travel to Versailles for her marriage to Louis Auguste, Dauphin of France, her cavalcade included 57 carriages, each drawn by six horses and preceded by three postillions. Two great wagons, each containing all the furnishings for a bedroom went in front of the procession. They proceeded in relays so that at each stopping place the young girl could find one of the two bedrooms with its armchairs, screens and folding stools in crimson damask "enriched with fringes, gold braid and gold embroidered cushions." Her two beds were both covered with scarlet satin together with a white satin coverlet.

Just 23 years later, the thirty-seven-year-old grey-haired "Widow Capet" stood in front of a prison table and turned in to the Recorder a small bundle of clothes, containing all her worldly possessions. The Recorder allowed her to keep the little gold watch she had brought with her from Austria and the clothes on her back. A few days later she wrote to her daughter from her death cell at Palais de Justice and history records that Madame Royale sent to her mother some "chemises trimmed with lace known as mignonettes, two pairs of black silk stockings, a mantle, three lawn fichus and a pair of shoes." She also obtained a bottle of dentifrice, a box of powder and a puff. So that she could keep her possessions from getting dusty, Rosalie, her guard, lent her a pasteboard box which she "received with as much satisfaction as if she had been lent the most beautiful piece of furniture in the world."

Let us hope that the pasteboard box Rosalie brought to Marie Antoinette was covered with a gay and bright wallpaper, for the death cell was a dreary place. It dripped with damp and was lit by a single window; its walls were half-covered with "hangings of paper nailed to frames."

The wallpaper covering the bandbox here illustrated would have been a design familiar to the unhappy Queen of France. It displays a pineapple

Red, white and green on a blue field with small white dots
14 x 8½, 7″ deep   No. 74   Circa 1835
                                                        Paper is probably earlier

Gift of Mr. J. Watson Webb, Jr., Los Angeles, California

(sign of hospitality) ensconced in an open-work basket with swan handles. The swan was known as the "bird royal" and with its graceful curving neck appears in some of the earliest wallpaper panels printed by Reveillon at his Royal Manufactory "Folie Titon" in Paris. Reveillon's chief contribution to the development of wallpaper was the execution of panels of such a character that they could be used to build into wood-panelled rooms, in place of decorations painted to order on canvas or wood.

See the bandbox illustrated on page 6 for another version of the pineapple and also page 5 for a bandbox with a swan-handle basket.

Metallic Rocaille Designs

This tiny trinket box carries out a nautical theme with its assortment of embossed spirula, triton and trumpet-shells, cockles, helices, nautilus, coral branches, whelks, scallops, snail and other sea animals and shells. When acquired by the museum, the prized possession of its past owner was still inside the box—six brilliant, shimmering peacock feathers.

Greenish-gold metallic paper

6 x 4, 3½″ deep   No. 15   Circa 1838.

The paper covering the box is one of the gold or bronze-finished papers made by first printing with size, and while still tacky, dusting over with bronze powder. A hare's foot was often used for a brush. A particularly fine effect was gained by applying an imitation gold leaf after this sizing operation. This metal, sometimes called Mosaic Gold or Dutch Metal, was made in Germany from an amalgam of tin and copper. After treatment the papers were embossed, and the resultant product had a rich and luxurious appearance.

Inside the top of this box is a little hand-painted water color of the famous steamboat *Great Western*. This is illustrated on page 125.

Scallop Shells

This bandbox is covered with a block-printed wallpaper featuring octagon cartouches framed with a band of small scallop shells. Inside the cartouche is a balanced design incorporating a single huge scallop and two shells of the gastropod or univalve class set in a dotted background.

The bivalve sea mollusks we know as scallops have two fan-shaped shells, usually ribbed or covered with radiating ridges and hinged together. They skitter about in the water by rapidly flipping open and snapping shut these shells. In the middle ages, the empty shells were used as a badge signifying the wearer had taken part in a pilgrimage to the shrine of St. James at Compostella or in one of the Crusades to the Holy Land. More recently the shells have served as a receptacle for baking a particular type of delicacy in which meat, vegetables or seafood is mixed with milk and crumbs, seasoned and baked until brown. We still speak of "scalloped potatoes" or a "scallop of oysters" even though now these delicacies are usually baked in casseroles. The scallops which we serve in a crusty French-fried coating of crumbs are the adductor muscle of the mollusk which opens and closes the shell.

The spiral shells on this bandbox paper are Triton's Trumpets, a particularly rich and handsome variety of the geometrically increasing cone shell coiled on its own axis. In ancient Greek mythology, the sea god Triton blew on one of these trumpet shells to ruffle the waters. They are still used as trumpets by some Pacific Island tribes and different tones are obtained by blowing on Tritons of varying sizes. It has been said that a "thirty-piece all-Triton instrument orchestra sounds exactly like a rich cathedral organ."

Blue, white and dark blue varnish on tan background

17 x 13, 11" deep   No. 135   Circa 1845

Block-printed wallpaper in pink, white and brilliant green varnish on faded yellow field

18 x 14½, 12″ deep   No. 35   Circa 1833

Cockatoo

The wallpaper covering the two boxes here illustrated shows the same design, but by a complete substitution of colors, the patterns appear to be different. Also one of the papers has been pasted to the box in a vertical position, rather than in a horizontal placement of the bird pattern. It is interesting to note that the bandbox made by "L. Bailey, band-box manufacturer, Brookline, N. H. (Band-boxes made to any pattern at short notice. Milliners supplied on favorable terms.)" carries the same cockatoo wallpaper that covers one of the bandboxes made by Hannah Davis, of Jaffrey, New Hampshire (illustrated on page 4). These two communities are both situated near the Massachusetts border and are within 25 miles of each other. Hannah's box shows a blue background and the Bailey box is printed on yellow. The third cockatoo box has a pink background.

Thin wood box above is lined with a copy of the *Globe*, published in Washington, D. C. and dated February 18, 1833.

The Parker History of Brookline (formerly Raby, Hillsborough County) New Hampshire which was published by the town around 1915 has been

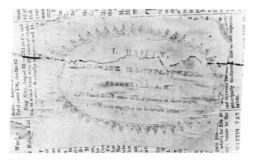

consulted in an effort to identify "L. Bailey, of Brookline, N. H." Although there are a number of genealogies as well as a chapter on local business, L. Bailey does not appear in this publication.

Bandbox on facing page, made of pasteboard, is lined with a copy of the *Courier & Enquirer*, published

Gift of Miss Katrina Kipper, Accord, Massachusetts.

Block-printed wallpaper in black, white and blue on a pink field.

15 x 12½, 11½" deep

No. 61   Circa 1838

in New York City by Col. J. Watson Webb, a forbear of one of the founders of Shelburne Museum. This newspaper dates February 16, 1838.

The chinoiserie designs on these wallpaper-covered bandboxes, the stylized cockatoos, flowering shrubs, roses, tulips and other nature patterns, are clearly related to the imported Chinese "birds and flowers" wallpapers of the 18th century. Bird motifs as ceramic decorations, particularly on Chelsea and Worcester porcelains, are well known and corresponding bird forms frequently appear in the copperplate-printed English and French textiles of that era.

While preparing about five years ago for an exhibition of English textiles in Manchester, England, a mass of important documentary material in the form of sample books put out by makers and vendors of the early chintzes from about 1760 through 1840 came to light. Illustrated in an old pattern book issued by Bromley Hall was a copperplate impression quite similar to our bandbox paper covering the boxes here illustrated. It was labelled "Cockatoo 10d a yard, Talwin & Foster." Certain of the copperplate impressions found in these books showed identifiable Chinese species of birds, such as the Cockatoo design, but many of the long-tailed "exotics" were inventions of the designer, rather than transcriptions from an ornithologist's records.

Peacock

This panel is a fragment of a bandbox and the design shows a peacock perched in a tree with grapes and roses in background. Printed in red and white on a blue background.

18½ x 11″   Panel No. 37   Circa 1835

The Peacock (Pavo Cristatus) is the most magnificent of the whole feathered creation. It was introduced into Europe from the south of Asia more than 2,000 years ago. It lives about 20 years, and does not acquire its beautiful plumage till three years of age.

—Goodrich's *Pictorial Geography*, published 1840.

The peacock, now so common in this country is of eastern origin and has been the admiration of all ages from that of King Solomon "Every three years once came the ships of Tarshish bringing gold and silver, ivory, asses and peacocks"—II Chron. ix, 21—to the present. Found in a wild state in many parts of Africa and Asia, but are no where so large as in India in the neighbourhood of the Ganges, from whence by degrees they have spread into all parts, increasing in a wild state in the warm climes but wanting some care in the colder regions. They seem to prefer the most elevated places to roost on of nights, such as high trees, tops of houses, and the like. Their cry is loud and inharmonious, a perfect contrast to their external beauty. The life of this bird is reckoned by some at about 25 years, by others 100. They average about three feet eight inches in length.

—Godey's *Lady Book* for October 1832. One of the entries in their series on birds published throughout the year 1832.

NATURAL AND GEOMETRICAL DESIGNS

Fashions

Engraving hand-tinted with watercolors

10″ diameter   Top to Box No. 98   Circa 1835

Really enormous bandboxes were required for the hats and bonnets of the 1830's. Godey's *Lady Book*, (July 1834), described a turban of white and blue gauze of moderate size with folds disposed with lightness and grace; a bandeau of gauze riband over the forehead passed under the turban at the sides and terminated in long ends floating over the neck. As a post-script to this be-ribboned turban, a white ostrich feather, tipped with blue was added.

In the same issue, fashion notes from the Paris correspondent pointed out:

The brims of hats increase in size; a new shape has just been brought out with a brim deeper than any that has appeared this season; very wide over the forehead and long at the ears. The crown is high and very little smaller at top than bottom. The inside of the brim is trimmed with riband and blond lace. The crown may be adorned with feathers, flowers or ribands, but whatever the trimming is, it is placed far back and two ends of riband which make part of it fall upon the shoulder. . . . Fashionable colours are rose, ruby, lilac, orange, pale blue, dark green, a new and brilliant shade of light green and citron. This last colour which used to be adopted only by ladies of a certain age, is this year worn even by the youngest married ladies.

In August of 1834 the fashion editor described a hat imported from Paris which was made of leghorn and ornamented with four superb white feathers, arranged in a most elegant and picturesque manner:

The longest dropped over the brim of the hat and the others were placed more erect so as to be agitated by the slightest breath of wind. . . . In Paris, a bird of paradise feather is not unfrequently worn in a leghorn hat.

These hats were fashioned to be worn over some of the most elaborate hair-dos ever designed.

The hair, parted on the forehead, is disposed in light loose curls which hang low at the sides. The hind hair is arranged in low bows, from which a few ringlets fall over the back of the head. The back hair is in two high coques or bows, encircled at the base with a rich bracelet, which also retains a long ostrich feather. . . . The front hair is very much parted on the forehead, the curls falling low at the sides. . . . The hair is divided on the forehead, falls in loose curls at the sides of the face, and is combed up tight to the summit of the head where it is arranged in a cluster of light bows, in which a sprig composed of coloured gems is inserted.

Illustrated here are a few of the "Milliner's models" in the Shelburne Museum doll collection which demonstrate the variety of "Apollo knots" and other elaborate hair fashions in vogue during the 1830's. Shown on page 69 is cover to bandbox on page 186.

Dianthus and Summer Flowers

A comparison of the floral forms incorporated in the wallpaper covering the boxes here illustrated with the bouquets depicted on page 73 would surely lead one to believe that the same artist's hand was responsible for both designs.

Pink, white and olive green varnish on a yellow field

20 x 15, 12½" deep

No. 33   Circa 1835

Thin wood box, pink, white and green varnish on blue background

20 x 16, 12½" deep

No. 99   Circa 1835

Top to box shown on page 174. Pink, white and green varnish on yellow background

17½ x 13½"   Top to box No. 95

Circa 1835

Here the large bouquet contains chrysanthemums (to the Chinese this flower symbolized gentility, nobility and longevity—the Chrysanthemum Viewing Party was inaugurated by Emperor Kao-tsu of the Han Dynasty during the year 200 B.C.); blue flags or iris (whose roots, according to Dioscorides are "causers of sleep and provokers of tears and heal the torments of the belly"— even today a derivitive is sometimes prescribed for jaundice); mock orange (the generic name *Philadelphus coronarius* honors Ptolemy Philadelphus, King of Egypt, 285–247 B.C. who held his banquets amidst lavish gardens—*coronarius* implies "suitable for garlands or wreaths"—hence our acceptance of orange blossoms in bridal flowers) and poppies (A grain of opium taken in the body mortifieth all the wits of man in such manner that he feeleth no pain and causeth him to sleep—so it is claimed in *The Grete Herball*). These bouquets are separated from each other by a small single stalk of the grass pink or dianthus. This low-growing plant has narrow bluish gray-green and powdery leaves which grow in dense tufts. The flowers have finely fringed petals of pinkish to purple. They have been popular here in America since the beginning—Thomas Jefferson planted them in his garden and Boston newspapers advertised them as early as 1760.

Primroses and Spring Bulbs

The boxes here illustrated feature a stalk of primroses and a group of spring flowers—tulips, jonquil and buds, set off in a curving woody branch intertwined with forget-me-nots. Floral motifs were used frequently on ceramics and later on in textiles and in wallpapers such as can be seen covering these bandboxes. The tulip has been accepted as a Christian symbol for many centuries. One of the myths attached to the forget-me-not tells of the lover who fell into a deep pool while gathering some of the tiny blue flowers for his sweetheart. As he sank forever, he threw a bunch of them on the bank, calling out "forget-me-not." An American herbalist maintains that the primrose flowers are useful in ordinary headache. The whole plant is supposed to have a somewhat soothing and quieting influence. The flowers and leaves cut small or granulated (one teaspoonful) are added to a cup of boiling water. When cold, a large mouthful may be drunk at a time until one cupful has been finished. An English herbalist, John Hill, M.D. wrote in 1756 that the roots of the common primrose are used as a "sternutatory against disease of the head . . . the juice when snuffed up occasions violent sneezing and when dried and powdered it is reported to be a cure in the night-mare."

Tall bandbox with top and lower section covered in this wallpaper pattern, when acquired included a clipping telling of the death of Miss Ann Augustus Clowes at the age of 95 in 1924. Miss Clowes was from one of the first settled families of Hempstead, New York. Her bonnet was also in the box.

Pink, white and light amber varnish on salmon pink background

28″ x 11   Panel No. 26   Circa 1835

Pink, white, olive green varnish on yellow background

15 x 12, 10¾″ deep
No. 11   Circa 1835

Pink, tan, white and blue on a white field

Round 12″ diameter, 15″ deep   No. 19   Circa 1835

Lilacs, Roses and Tulips

On the paper covering this bandbox, detached sprays of lilacs, roses and tulips printed in yellow and red are framed by winding branches bearing triangular leaves and red berries. Both single and double roses are included and the sprays are all in a large scale.

The bottom of the box is lined with a copy of the German-language newspaper *Der Freiheits-Wachter* for December 7, 1836. This newspaper was published in Skippacksville, in Montgomery County, near Philadelphia, Pennsylvania. The earliest imprint of *Der Freiheits-Wachter* on file in the fine collection of Pennsylvania-German imprints in the rare book department of the Free Library of Philadelphia, is one from 1835.

Much of the material in newspapers and books published by the Pennsylvania-Dutch, as might be expected of a people who had left their native Rhine Valley to find freedom of worship, is of a predominantly religious inclination. However, these printers are also known for their charming A B C Children's Books, which one early collector of German imprints has characterized as differing from New England primers in that they "say little of hell, but much of heaven."

Yellow and Indian red on dark blue
background

18 x 14, 12½" deep

No. 123   Circa 1836

Summer Flowers

This pasteboard box has a heavy wood bottom and top and is covered with block-printed wallpaper in green, blue, black, tan and pink on a cream ground.

A beautiful bouquet of mid-summer flowers has been arranged in a flat broad pattern and enclosed in a band printed with imitation stucco molding to make the charming border wallpaper on this box. An unusually large number of blocks would have been used to make the design on this paper, as each of the colors was applied with a separate wooden block. Usually on the papers on the bandboxes only three blocks were required, but here five have been used. In 1849, Zuber used two thousand blocks to print the twenty strips of "Eldorado" in color, and Dufour's masterpiece, "Les Amours de Psyche" which won the Grand Prix de Rome in 1791, employed fifteen hundred wood blocks to print the 26 strips in grisaille and sepia. After Dufour's death, the blocks were purchased by Désfossé et

Karth, and today modern editions of this masterwork, consisting of twelve complete pictures are still being issued.

Round, 10″ in diameter, 5″ deep

No. 120

About 1835

Flower Cluster

Thin wooden box, partially lined with newspapers and covered with wallpaper, exhibits a flat triple cluster of flowers framed with a meandering chalky-white leaf design. White dots fill in the intermediate spaces.

Green, pink, red and green varnish on yellow field

8½ x 6, 4½″ deep

No. 44   Circa 1835

Floral Varieties

The large bandbox here illustrated is covered with a wallpaper featuring interlacing chalky white borders framing floral bouquets and a compote spilling a variety of fruits. The floral designs differ from one another and include carnations, lilies, dahlias, roses and other types. This box has been relined with a modern wallpaper with red and white stripes on a gray background.

Pink, white and green varnish on bright blue background

18 x 13. 11" deep   No. 154   Circa 1835

Gay Garden

This thin wooden bandbox has been lined with plain white paper and covered with wallpaper in pink, red, white and green varnish on a blue field. The paper, incorporating a chrysanthemum and a rose has been reproduced by Miss Nancy McClelland of New York and issued under the title of "Gay Garden."

In the old days, hand-carved wooden blocks would have been used to print the design on the paper, but today when these papers are reproduced, the silk screen method is used. A silk screen is a mesh of silken strands fixed to a plastic cellophane-type of sealer. The design is transferred to the screen by cutting through the sealer, but not through the silk mesh. The areas which are to print the design are thus opened up on the frame of thin silk so that paint will pass through. The wallpaper (to which the ground color has already been applied mechanically) is stretched on a long table. The silk screen is positioned on the paper and with a squeegee or blade the paint is pushed from one side of the screen to the other. The paint passes through the open areas of the screen but not through the balance of the plastic-sealed surface. The worker then moves the screen on to the next interval where the repeat of the pattern requires this portion of the design. A separate screen is required for each print color, and consequently the number of print colors is usually kept to a minimum on these reproduced papers. Each color must be allowed to dry before the next is applied. The silk screen process is in reality a refinement of the stencil printing method.

The newspaper pasted to the bottom of this bandbox is dated 1835.

Gift of Miss Nancy McClelland, New York

11 x 8, 5½" deep   No. 72   Circa 1835

Daisy Chain

The daisies in this border pattern are arranged in a chain pattern and the paper would have been cut between the double center line when it was used as a running border about a room.

This pretty perennial flower has been known from time immemorial and is often mentioned in literature. Chaucer called it the "eye of day," and Spenser, Bacon and Shakespeare all speak of it with affection. The name of the flower—daisy, comes from the old Anglo-Saxon "day's eye" and is the pet name of the "bellis compositae" mentioned in Mrs. Loudon's *Companion to the Flower-Garden* book on gardening for ladies published in its New York edition in 1843. She points out that this flower has been in cultivation in British and Continental gardens for many years and that in Germany they have raised numerous varieties by saving the seed of the handsomest kinds. Mr. A. J. Downing edited the American edition and added "These pretty plants are seldom seen in our gardens in as great abundance as they deserve, which is owing no doubt to their being very impatient of our hot summers. They should therefore be grown in a shady and rather cool border."

This box is lined with copies of *The Newburyport Herald* for 1828 and 1830.

Tan, brown and white on a grey background with border of lavender which has been added with tempera by a previous owner.

18 x 10, 9" deep

No. 118   Circa 1830

Passion Flower

A variety of curious and alien flowers are depicted on the wallpaper which covers this bandbox, among which can be identified the passion flower or passion vine with its deeply cleft leaves and simple axillary tendrils with which it climbs. Flowers are almost white except for the purple center and the blue crown banded with white in the middle. A species is found in the southern United States which bears an edible, but insipid, fruit called "maypop."

White, pink and green varnish on yellow field

19 x 14½, 13″ deep   No. 36   Circa 1840

Pasted to this thin wood box on the bottom is a fragment of newspaper which shows the official notice from the U.S. Navy Department dated July 11, 1839 listing the 29 midshipmen who had passed the exam held on June 24th at the Naval Asylum in Philadelphia.

Flower Garden

A wallpaper such as the one pictured on this bandbox would have been a practical choice for a home, except that it was so dark in background color. In all probability it would have been used as a border at the top of the room. One of the super-salesmen who advertised in the Philadelphia newspaper toward the end of the 19th century pointed out that "smoke will not considerably affect the dark colors in the course of 20 years." This bandbox has been steamed open and mounted on panel.

Pink, white and amber varnish on dark blue field

28 x 10″   Panel No. 25   Circa 1835

Shaded Design Papers

ACANTHUS LEAF AND MEDALLION

The wallpaper covering this thin wood box is of the Greek Revival era and shows a classical design of medallion and acanthus leaves. The diagonal over-print shading is common to this type of design and adds depth and a three-dimensional feeling to the pattern.

Red, tan on a blue field

20 X 15, 13″ deep   No. 68   Circa 1825

HILLSBOROUGH SUPERIOR COURT.

APRIL TERM, 1825.

CONTINUED ACTIONS.

Brown.
1. John Grimes *v* William Clark, jr. & a.
   Exre,

J. Harris.   *B. Chase.*
2. Aaron W. Buswell & a. *v* David Fellows.
   Defaulted. Deft. to be heard in damages.

Brown.   *Haselton.*
3. Susanna West *v* Joseph Alcock & a.
   April 1822, referred.

Bowman.   *Wilkins.*
4. Daniel Parker *v* Peter Foster.
   Leave to amend. April 1824, Verdict, Deft. guilty.
   Dam. $406 67. Motion for new trial.

Wilkins.   *Bowman.*
5. Hugh Moors *v* Jonathan Palmer.
   Oct. 1822, defaulted.   Judgment.

Wilkins.   *Bowman.*
6. Henry Rice *v* Jonathan Palmer.
   Oct. 1822 defaulted.   Judgment.

Wilkins.   *Bowman.*
7. Hugh Moors *v* Jonathan Palmer.
   Oct. 1822, defaulted.   Judgment.

Glidden.
8. Samuel Searles Petition for partition.
   For notice.

A copy of the Hillsborough County, New Hampshire Superior Court April Term 1825 continued actions has been used to paper the bottom of this box. Political economists of today tell us that our present-day high standard of living is produced by our liberality and prodigal use of resources. In the first half of the 19th century, however, financial tycoons advocated the opposite form of organization of our production and distribution of national wealth. Instead of "throw-away" economy, the custom was "save, use over, make do." Because of this practice newspapers and other printed materials were used to line and reinforce these hat boxes and today we find the secondary material as interesting as the wallpaper covering the box itself.

SHADED WILDROSE

Graceful stems containing wild rose blooms wind up and down the paper covering this box in an all-over printed design.

Grey and white on a yellow field

11½ x 9½, 7″ deep

No. 63   Circa 1825

SHADED ARABESQUES

An arabesque is a form of ornament, Arabian in style, and often consists of fanciful or purely imaginary men and animal forms, sometimes truncated and growing out of the curves. In its purest style, however, figures of animals were excluded as they were forbidden by the Koran. Plants, fruits,

foliage, involved, contorted and twisted, used either alone or as objects upon which other objects rest were acceptable. The arabesques were used for engraving flat surfaces and could be inlaid in mosaic work, carved in low relief or painted. As an art motif, they probably reached their greatest vogue under the Kings of France, Louis XV and Louis XVI.

Pale green and tan varnish on a beige background

8½ x 7½, 5½″ deep

No. 115   Circa 1844

Paper is probably earlier

The arabesques on this box are combined with stylized floral forms, and the bottom of the box has been reinforced with newspapers dating from 1844.

Wood Anemones

And at the root through lush green grasses,
Burned the red anemone . . . Dream of Fair Women.
—Tennyson

There are three bandboxes in the museum collection featuring this lovely design of wood anemones or windflowers framed with a winding serpentine border of small flowers and foliage. The *anemone Quinquefolia* (referring to the five-petalled form of the bloom) has been described in a herbal materia medica book as an exceedingly delicate-looking plant, common in our woods with a slender stem from four to eight inches high and a solitary flower, white inside and purplish on the outer surface. It has been used, continues this little book, "by eclectic physicians, but its virtues are said to depend upon its effect as a local irritant."

Mrs. J. C. Loudon's treatise *Gardening for Ladies* and its second section *A Companion to the Flower-Garden* met with such a favorable reception in England that the third London edition was edited by A. J. Downing and published in a first American edition in 1843. She was fond of the anemone and mentioned that all the plants belonging to that genus are beautiful and well deserving of cultivation—from the little white wood anemone to the largest Dutch varieties. However, she warned:

> Garden anemones, called Florists' flowers, require the utmost care in their cultivation. . . . The tubers of these fine kinds of anemones, and their hybrids

11 x 10, 6″ deep	17 x 13½, 11½″ deep
No. 39 Circa 1830	No. 10 Circa 1830

and varieties are sold in the seed-shops by the hundred. They resemble little bunches of small black potatoes, which may be divided, each portion producing a new plant, though it will probably be too weak to flower the first year. As *A. coronaria*, which is the parent of the finest florists' anemones comes from Syria and Asia Minor, where the ground is parched and dry in the hot season, the tubers should be taken up every summer, as soon as the flowers are over and the leaves have turned yellow.

The bandboxes covered with the anemone wallpaper design vary in size, but all are printed with pink, white and green varnish onto the blue background.

On the bottom of one of the boxes, the name, Samuel Brower, has been stencilled. A search of the New York city directories discloses that Mr. Brower is first listed as a bandbox maker in 1815 at 108 William Street. In 1817 he moved to 125 William Street and the following year transferred his business to the 127 address. From 1819 through 1820 he identified himself as a "bandbox and trunk maker," but in all his other listings he is registered as a bandbox maker. His name continues to appear in directories through 1830 but apparently he died in that year for the 1830–31 directory lists "Charlotte Brower, widow of Samuel, bandbox maker" at 127 William Street, New York.

14 x 10½, 9½" deep

No. 65   1818–30

Sunflower

Oval bandbox top glued to rectangular board. Wallpaper covering the box top has been printed in red, pink and amber varnish on the blue background. The bloom has been set in an elliptic panel which has been banded by a rectangle of chalky white foliage with a rosette in each corner. Beyond the centered sunflower winds an ivy leaf design. Small dots have been added to further enhance the pattern.

Panel 19 x 15″ Top No. 12   Circa 1835

In 1786, an astute Philadelphia wallpaper manufacturer, in order to compete with the admittedly finer imported wall coverings, advertised that he had for sale a new type of paper. He stated that "Flies and smoke operate to soil paper in common rooms if the goods are too delicate; to prevent which I have pin grounds that fly marks will not be perceptible upon!" The dots around the outside of this cover are larger than fly-speck size, but they would have tended to camouflage finger marks to some extent where the cover had been repeatedly lifted from the box.

Camellia

The lovely camellia double flowers in red, pink or white are sometimes known as the Japan Rose. Unfortunately most of the varieties are not hardy above Charleston, South Carolina so they must be cultivated in greenhouses if raised in this part of the country. The Camellia was named for George Joseph Kamel, the 17th century Jesuit priest and traveler, who first described the flower.

A border design featuring camellias has been used on the sides of one of the boxes in the museum collection and on the top of another of the boxes shown on this page. This box features a somewhat later paper on the sides than the camellia paper on the top.

Round thin wood box with paper bottom and cardboard top (below), is covered with block-printed wallpaper in green, tan, yellow and brown on a blue background.

7½ x 8½"   Top of box No. 115

Circa 1835

Round, 9" diameter, 6½" deep   No. 102

About 1835

Swirl Flower

The flowers spaced in rows on this box have eight swirled petals with yellow centers. It is an all-over printed paper and the same design appears both on the top of the box and on the sides.

The newspapers lining the box are copies of *The State Capitol Gazette*, a Pennsylvania newspaper filled with political chit-chat and some extracts— "Precious Jewels" selected from the *Lutheran Observer*.

The bandbox was made by Sarah Weaver of Walker Township, Juniata County, Pennsylvania. County histories covering Juniata County have been checked, but there is no reference to Sarah Weaver and Juniata not having a heavy population does not seem to have stimulated anyone to produce a county directory or county atlas in which a trade list might have been included.

However, according to the tradecard pasted in the top of the box, the card was printed by "J. Myers, Printer." This was probably Jacob Myers, who in addition to being a printer, was also a doctor, druggist and newspaper publisher. His newspaper was first a German paper under the title *Juniata Valley Herichter*, and later was renamed *Juniata Aurora and Perry and Mifflin County Advertiser*. He established the newspaper in Mifflintown in September of 1839 and in the spring of 1841 sold it out. Maybe Sarah Weaver advertised in his newspaper, but Pennsylvania Historical and Museum Commission was unable to locate any copies of this paper.

Orange and yellow on a blue background

17 x 13, 12″ deep

No. 130   Circa 1840

Bride's Box

Splint wooden boxes similar to this one, painted in bright primary colors were well known around the Pennsylvania-Dutch countryside. They were intended for keeping wearing apparel and often were presented by a man to his intended bride as a gift in which to store her more fragile items of the trousseau. They were also known as gift boxes and dressing boxes and are said to continue a tradition of European peasant art.

In the old country they were sometimes painted by experts and many probably came over as baggage with immigrants, for quite naturally they were prized for sentimental reasons. Occasionally we find one that has been made locally; sometimes there is no inscription and the box is sparsely decorated, but usually there is a very tender sentiment lettered on in old German text. In Europe they were known as "Spahn Schacteln" or chip boxes and many seem to have come from Bavaria.

Usually the ones that portray a man and woman were gifts from a fiancé, and the little couplet on this box is a reminder from the groom that his heart will belong to the bride alone.

18 x 12, 9″ deep

No. 159

19th century

Minikins, or Miniature Band Boxes

There is an entrancing group of diminutive bandboxes answering the meaning of the obsolete word, "minikin"—which was "a darling; something very small and delicate." These boxes would have been used to store ribbons, artificial flowers or other trinkets—those trifles, ornaments and "pretend jewels" preserved by women as souvenirs of some special occasion or just in case they might come back in style. While acting as a case or container the boxes also created their own spot of color on milady's shelf or chest.

UNDULATE FOLIAGE BAND

Pasteboard box covered with Empire border wallpaper showing an interlacing broad foliage band passing over and under another ribbon band punctuated with single leaf motifs. Colors are green, pink, orange and white on a yellow field.

Newspapers lining this box announce sailings of the schooner *Lucretia* to Halifax, Nova Scotia; the sloop *Betsey* to Wilmington, North Carolina, and the brig *Pleides* for New Orleans.

6¼ x 5, 3″ deep

No. 16   Circa 1818

DRUM

Pasteboard box covered with block-printed wallpaper in pink, white and green varnish on yellow background. The large-scale wallpaper pasted to the sides of this drum-shaped box is a different design from the centered single flower motif on the cover of the box.

Round, 2¾″ diameter, 2″ deep

No. 18   Circa 1818

Round, 6" diameter, 4" deep No. 45   Circa 1835

SPIRALS

This pasteboard box has a thin wood bottom and is covered with a corkscrew design block-printed on wallpaper. This was a popular motif and is often found in very strong oranges, yellows, blues and greens. This example is printed in a strident combination of orange and black on a blue background.

HUMMING BIRD

Thin wooden box, lined with scraps of newspaper, is covered with yellow, white and pink designs on chocolate brown background.

The tiny humming bird on the top of the box has been hand-painted on the wallpaper flowering stalk decorating the sides of the box. Humming birds have small heads, tiny jet black eyes and their feet are so puny and weak that they will not support the weight of the bird on flat surfaces; consequently one usually sees them hovering in the air while feeding or in flight with wings moving so rapidly that they appear as a blur.

Their nests, about the size of a hen's egg cut in two and composed of cotton or fine moss, are hung in the air attached to twigs on low trees. The

4 x 3, 2½" deep

No. 17

Circa 1835

humming bird lays each year two eggs, about the size of small peas and as white as snow, with here and there a yellow speck; and at the end of 12 days the young appear.

There are about 750 species of these brilliantly colored New World birds, but only the ruby-throated humming bird is found in the northern United States. The majority of the species are native to Central and South America.

BORDER STRIPES

Pasteboard box is lined with plain grey paper and covered with paper printed in shades of rose-red, green and black on a tan ground. There is a border design on sides of box and floral paper on top. A newspaper from the City of Philadelphia bearing a January 1801 date has been pasted to outside bottom.

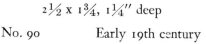

$2\frac{1}{2}$ x $1\frac{3}{4}$, $1\frac{1}{4}''$ deep

No. 90   Early 19th century

Gift of Mr. John A. H. Sweeney, Winterthur, Delaware

CUT-APART BORDERS

Pasteboard box is covered with remnants of border strip paper. On sides paper is printed in orange, pink on a black ground. The cover has paper printed in green and red on black field—this is not a matching pattern.

Round, $3\frac{1}{2}''$ diameter, $2\frac{1}{2}''$ deep   No. 47   Circa 1835

6½ x 3½, 2¾″ deep

No. 122

Early 19th century

SPORT

This thin wooden box is covered with block-printed paper tinted with colors. The sides of the box are covered with paper in a floral pattern of carnations and roses; on the top of the box is a scene of children at play and this view has been labeled "Sport." Paper has darkened with age.

HEART-SHAPED BOX

The huge bonnets and hats of the 1830 period were often worn over an embroidered, lace-trimmed sheer muslin cap called a lingerie cap or "cornet." Fashionable women wore headcoverings, whether indoors or outside. Close caps of embroidered tulle were used for morning wear and sheer, dainty lace caps were donned for night wear. There were "rising caps" and "theatre caps"—the latter heavily embroidered over lace. We are told that during this period the small bandbox returned to favor and was used by the ladies to carry their little caps to the theatre. Once there, they removed their immense bonnets or hats and substituted the little cornet cap which had been neatly transported in a prettily decorated box such as here illustrated. This heart-shaped box has been covered in wallpaper of a classic medallion or rosette design and is lined with a Montpelier, Vermont newspaper dated December 2, 1833.

7 x 6, 2½″ deep

No. 85   Circa 1835

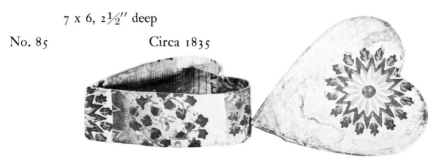

Block-printed in red, grey, blue and green varnish on an ombre shaded field

FLOWER SPRAY

Small size trinket box in pasteboard is covered with block-printed wallpaper in pink, white, yellow and green varnish on blue field.

The newspaper lining this box is one published by the Unitarians about 1830. In this country, Unitarianism had its birth in the Congregational churches of New England and in many communities was an off-shoot of the sterner Calvinistic Congregational concept of religion. The American Unitarian Association was formed in 1825. Unitarians believe in a conception of God as one person, in distinction to the orthodox doctrine of the triune nature of God. Neither ministers nor members are required to make profession of a particular doctrine and no creed has ever been adopted by the church. The covenant in general use is simply—"In the love of truth, and in the spirit of Jesus, we unite for the worship of God and the service of man."

Round, 6" diameter, 4½" deep   No. 57   Circa 1830

Cornucopia with Fruits and Flowers

This oval bandbox top, illustrated at the top of the next page, mounted on a rectangular panel shows two cornucopias overflowing with grapes, peaches, roses and other flowers. A basket is centered between the two curving horns and this too is well-supplied with a profusion of floral forms. Designs on the cover are block printed in pink, white and amber varnish on the yellow background.

Panel 19 x 15″

Oval top No. 3

Circa 1830

Cornucopia with Flowers

The wallpaper covering this box uses for its dominant pattern the cornucopia filled with flowers. The cornucopia motif was frequently used in symbolizing America's plenty, abundance and prosperity; in fact the two Latin roots from which the word was derived mean "horn of plenty."

Immigrants to this country did indeed find here a land of plenty, compared with the over-populated districts from which they had come. Oppor-

Thin wood box covered with block-printed wallpaper in yellow, pink, white and green varnish on blue ground

15 X 11, 10″ deep   No. 34

Circa 1830

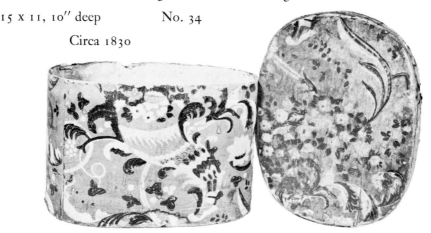

tunities existed for everyone to make his way in America and visitors remarked upon this fact more than once. An English tourist, Capt. Marryat, in 1839 wrote in his *Diary:*

> Let the American direct his career to any goal he pleases, his energies are unshackled and in the race the best man must win. There is room for all, and millions more. Let him choose his profession—his career is not checked or foiled by the excess of those who have already embarked in it. In every department there is an opening for talent; and for those inclined to work, work is always to be procured. You have no complaint in this country that every profession is so full that it is impossible to know what to do with your children. There is a vast field, and all may receive the reward due for their labor.

Pine Cone

The pineapple-like fruit used on this pasteboard bandbox with wooden bottom is related to the pomegranite, one of the oldest of the Persian designs. When Persia was added to the Mohammedan Empire, the motif was adopted there and through Constantinople migrated to Italy. Here it was somewhat altered, for designers in this European country were more familiar with the artichoke plant and the pine cone.

The black and white cone or fruit printed on an Indian red background is here enclosed in a rondelle with the colors alternating and looks contemporary in concept. However, the oldest scrap of wall paper ever found —the remnant on a beam of Christ's College, Cambridge, England placed there in 1509—incorporates the same two motifs, the rondelle enclosing a pine cone, pineapple or artichoke.

This juxtapositioned design in black and white has also been found on a deep blue background and Jones & Erwin of New York who have issued many reproductions of old wallpapers believe it to be American in origin.

8½ x 6, 5″ deep

No. 83

Circa 1820

16 x 11½, 9″ deep   No. 82   Circa 1812

"Providence House"

The bandbox here shown has been covered with the same wallpaper design found in the Old Market House in Providence, Rhode Island. This building is now part of the Rhode Island School of Design and the wallpaper has been reproduced by Nancy McClelland of New York in six color combinations. The original and the one on our bandbox were block-printed in red, orange and white on a gray background.

Stripes embodying four different designs can be seen here. The main design is a domed device with flowering branches springing from its roof in the Chinoiserie manner. Below this are arabesques and a dropped swag. This main motif is enclosed with wide stripes bound together with chevrons and adjoining these are graceful winding vines. Infinitesimal lily stripes separate the final band of Prince-of-Wales feather arrangements from the vines.

The same fashionable lady owned this box and the one illustrated on page 94. Newspapers from Providence, Rhode Island dating in 1811 and 1812 line the box.

18½ x 14½, 11½" deep   No. 79   Circa 1835

Palmate Leaf

This thin wood box is covered with an unusual block-printed wallpaper in red and yellow on a dark blue field. The design features a star shape or palmate leaf and is printed in an all-over pattern on both the sides and top of the box.

Newspapers dating from 1831 and 1834 have been used to line this box, as well as a copy of the *New Hampshire Sentinal* dated January 8th 1814 which spells out the New Embargo Act. The Embargo acts of 1807 and 1808 were especially protested in New England, but they represented a daring attempt by a small power to use economic pressure against two great powers in a world at war.

Napoleon in his economic warfare with England from 1806 to 1812 adopted the "Continental System" which forbade trade with Great Britain. England in answer to this restriction passed Orders in Council inhibiting neutral shipping. Not to be outdone, the U.S. Congress at President Jefferson's behest in 1807 passed an embargo act forbidding all international trade to and from America. It was hoped that this Act would persuade England and France of the value and rights of a neutral commerce. However the greatest opposition to the Act came from our own United States merchants, sea captains and sailors, who were dismayed to find themselves without income and their ships rotting at the wharves. The law was circumvented in many ways by the merchants who saw in it a scheme to defraud them of their livelihood. It was never really rigidly enforced and eventually was so watered down that it became ineffective. Jefferson's prestige was much hurt by the failure of his scheme.

Diaper, Scrolls, Flowers and Fruit

The interior of this box shows a coarse homespun linen lining around the sides and inside the top. On the bottom of the box are New Hampshire newspapers dating 1838 and 1839.

Red, white and green varnish on a yellow field

9 x 8, 4″ deep   No. 21   Circa 1840

Gift of Mrs. Katharine Prentis Murphy, New York

Before newspapers finished their life of usefulness as bandbox linings, they occupied a very special place in the hearts of all Americans. The citizens of this country were proud of their book-learning, and even where the parents were unable to read, they kept up to date on national happenings through their newspapers. *Farmer's Almanac* for February 1848 describes the almost ritualistic scene in front of the fire at the end of the day:

THE NEWSPAPER.

Now, after the work is all done up, the fire replenished and the lamps lighted, let us take seats and hear the newspaper read. Little Jethro is the boy for it, and when he is tired, Anna shall take her turn. Can there be a pleasanter sight than this? We now see the benefit of schooling. I see, Mr. Cleverly, that you have not neglected your duty in these matters. You have not been backward, as the manner of too many is; you have visited the school to see how the teacher gets along, and how the scholars improve; whether they are profitably engaged, love their books, and love their master, or are like calves, turned into a bush pasture, where, here and there, a few only are able to browse a little and get a scanty subsistence, while the rest hunger, and pine, on their fare. Now, look at these children and listen to their performance. How promptly and ready they are, and how understandingly they read! This shows that their teacher has taken the right course with his pupils, and applied rules to practice; and a very important one is, that the scholar should understand, or endeavor to understand, what he reads. Newspaper reading is the most difficult, because of its variety; yet these children are able to go through it, from beginning to end, with ease, because they have been taught correctly.

Still Life with Urn

This thin wooden box, one of the larger examples in the museum collection has been covered with a wallpaper featuring polygon panels with concave sides, alternating with a still life arrangement incorporating large urn, draped swag, up-turned bowl and crescent of floral forms. It has been lined with a copy of the *New Hampshire Sentinel* dated July 21, 1810.

Pink, white and green
varnish on blue field

18 x 13, 10″ deep

No. 29

Circa 1820

Columns and Carnations

A complicated pillar print wallpaper covers this bandbox. The twisted columns with elaborate capitals spouting acanthus leaves enclose strips displaying floral bouquets. The flowers include carnations, roses, chrysanthemums and dahlias.

We have come to accept the fact that a systematic examination of pattern books and surviving English printed textiles shows that the pillar print is one of the most characteristic and original contributions in the field of English printed textiles and it is not surprising that this print also found popularity as a wallpaper design. Indeed we have been told that in many cases the same wood blocks used for printing textiles were used to print wallpaper. Peter Floud of Victoria and Albert Museum in London in his article on the pillar print in British textiles published in *Antiques* magazine for October 1957 describes the variety to be found in the pillar prints:

> Every conceivable type of pillar was introduced into these designs—especially, of course, the "Gothic," for there was hardly any other way in which the normal chintz design could be adapted to suit the Gothic taste. In some cases a floral bouquet was centrally disposed so as to appear to be growing out from above the capital, but a more favored arrangement was for the flowers to form a spiral cascade encircling the pillar.

The first wave of popularity for the pillar prints appeared between 1800 and 1808 after which they went out of fashion. Between 1825 and 1830 the pillar print was revived as a vehicle for some of the finest roller-printed designs ever produced.

Dark blue and white on gray background

19 x 16½, 13″ deep

No. 139

Circa 1835

Festoon Papers

In the last years of the 18th century almost all of the newspaper notices advertising wallpaper mentioned patterns featuring festoon, swag, garland or drapery motifs. From 1807 through 1815 the factory of Joseph Dufour in Paris was noted for its drapery border papers and was proud of the variety of treatments of the half-circle motif they had for sale. In the American newspapers C. Alder of New York advertised in 1799 that he had for sale an elegant assortment of Paper Hangings, French, English and American Manufacture among them, some of the latest importations and newest patterns. The Crygiers of Water Street advertised their "plain green, plain blue . . . with an elegant assortment of rose and fruit borders to match—feather, festoon, etc." John Birch in 1787 mentioned his one hundred and fifty patterns of paper hangings, being a collection of the newest fashions, "With elegant Festoon Borders." John Colles of Dock Street also mentioned that same year in his advertisements his "large and elegant assortment of paper hangings, with Festoon borders."

Naturally the remnants of the festoon papers found on bandboxes show a like variety and illustrated here are several versions of festoon papers in the Shelburne Museum collection.

Decorative borders served a useful function in giving interest to the walls of a room, yet did not interfere with pictures, looking glasses or other wall decorations as in the case of wallpapers whose designs covered the wall surfaces. Sometimes the borders ran like a frieze around the top of the walls under the cornice; sometimes they were used above the dado or as substitutes for panel moldings. They could also outline panel designs, thus making the panel more important.

17 x 14, 10″ deep   No. 37

DRAPERY SWAG WITH ROSES

An identical design wallpaper was used on the crescent-shaped hat box containing the chapeau bras illustrated on page 25.

Pink, white and olive-green varnish on tan background

Probably 1830–35, Paper is earlier

DRAPERY SWAG WITH ROSETTE

A line divides the border designs and the paper would have been cut apart on this line when it was hung.

Double design of green draped swags caught up with a six-petalled rosette in yellow and brown

12 x 8¼″   Top of box No. 119   About 1830, Paper is earlier

DRAPERY SWAG WITH THREE ROSES AND VASE

The festoon papers could be further embellished with a baluster-shaped vase holding a single rose interrupting the festoon swags. On the fragment here shown, the space above the festoon is filled in with a triple rose design.

White, pink and amber varnish on green field

24 x 11″
Panel No. 23
Circa 1830

DRAPERY SWAG WITH TWO ROSES AND VASE

A paper similar to the one described above has been used to cover the top of one of the museum collection bandboxes. Here twin roses fill in the spaces above the drapery swag.

Pink, white and amber varnish on blue ground

16 x 12½″
Top of Box No. 77
Circa 1830

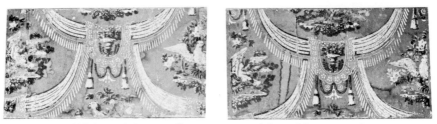

White, pink and olive-green varnish on blue ground

42 x 12″   Panel No. 24   Circa 1830

DRAPERY SWAG WITH TASSELS AND BIRDS

Here a pair of nesting birds are framed by the alternating drops of several swags which have been hung with a lacy "apron" caught with tassels.

DRAPERY SWAG WITH FLOWERS AND BIRDS

Bandbox covered with paper, featuring a floral nest with two birds hovering above, filling in the swag drop.

There is also a panel (No. 22) in the museum collection in this same design, but printed in red, white and amber varnish on a pale yellow field.

The box here shown was made by Nathaniel Smith for Giles Spencer. A search of the Troy, New York business directories has shown that Nathaniel Smith was first listed as a bandbox maker at 41 Congress Street in 1829. Directories of subsequent years give his occupation as letter carrier, constable and root doctor. In 1836 and 1837 he was again listed as a bandbox maker, but the following two years record his occupation as "pedler." His final inclusion in 1841 lists him as "confectioner."

Giles Spencer's name does not appear in the directories, but J. C. Spencer & Company had a hat store in 1836 and in 1838, John C. Spencer was listed as selling hats, caps and furs.

Trunks & Bandboxes,
MANUFACTURED BY
NATHANIEL SMITH,
At the factory corner of third and Congress
Streets, Troy, for GILES SPENCER.

Light and dark pink, white and amber varnish on gray background

17 x 14, 11″ deep

No. 165   Circa 1836

Oak Leaves and Acorns

The several varieties of oaks found growing in America when it was first settled each had their own medicinal and useful properties. The white oak, closest to the English oak provided acorns which could be boiled and eaten. The oil was sometimes skimmed off and used as a liniment to "supple the joynts." The bark of this tree was slightly tonic and very astringent, but was "useful and commonly employed as a wash and gargle for irritations of the mouth and throat." Black oak bark too was useful as an external astringent, but rarely was employed internally, as it was "liable to derange the bowels." However it was utilized in tanning and for dyeing. The bark of the red oak also contained considerable tannin (the finest harness leather was made of cow or steer hides, tanned with oak bark and curried with tallow and neatsfoot oil). The Indians ate the acorns of the live oak (a native oak ranging southward from Virginia along the coast to Mexico) with hominy and wild rice and ground them up to thicken their venison soup. The wood of the live oak, probably the heaviest and hardest of all the oaks, was valuable for making wagons, tool handles and in construction of wooden ships. White oak was also used in shipbuilding and for houses, furniture and in cooperage. White oak casks and barrels were judged best of all in this line.

Newspapers pasted inside this box date from 1830 and one of the fragments is from a Bellows Falls, Vermont newspaper dated Saturday October 11, 1834. This city, across the Connecticut River from Walpole, New Hampshire served in the old days as an important stage coach transfer point. Stages from Boston to Montreal were dispatched through here and then followed a north-western route which took them across Vermont to Basin Harbor where passengers could board one of the Lake Champlain steamers and complete their trip to Montreal.

Red, blue and green varnish on yellow background

11 x 10, 7½" deep

No. 113

Circa 1835

Variations on the Rosette Theme

The rosette design is in reality a treatment of the artificial rose and in a wider sense any ornament of a circular shape radiating from a center may be termed a rosette. It may be executed either as a free ornament or as a panel ornament and may have any number of divisions, but the odd-numbered divisions—seven, nine or eleven—are rare. Some of the modifications of the rosette form are shown on the bandbox papers here illustrated.

ROSETTE IN SQUARE PANEL

Rosette with eight divisions is filled in at edges with stylized tulip or lily pattern. The motif has been enclosed in a square bordered with heart-shaped motifs, set off at the corners with an eight-division rosette. Newspapers from Connecticut dating 1843 and 1844 are pasted to bottom of this box.

Green, black and white on tan background

10 x 9, 7" deep   No. 114   Circa 1845

ROSETTE BAND

This box is covered in a border pattern wallpaper and shows single rosettes extended in design with a palmette on either side of the motif. Alternating with this primary shape and filling in the intermediate spaces is a small rosette with six-pointed divisions.

Yellow, tan, blue green and brown on green background

12 x 8¼, 5" deep

No. 119

Circa 1835

ROSETTE IN
STRAPWORK FRAME

Black and white on a blue field

Round, 10" diameter, 8" deep

No. 112   Circa 1845

Elaborate frames cut into fantastic shapes and bands which interlace and curl are known in the field of ornament as "Strapwork Frames." Foliage, palmettes, festoons, garlands of fruit or fluttering ribbons are frequently added. An invention of the Renaissance and originally intended as a frame, now we frequently see the strapwork alone as a motif with the inside left as empty space. Here the strapwork frame on this bandbox encloses a symmetrical six-sided rosette. The box has been lined with newspapers dating from about 1845. One of these papers is a copy of the *Saturday Post*.

Blue, white on tan background

11 x 8½, 6" deep

No. 103

Circa 1849

DUODECAGONS AND SQUARES

Geometrical designs make up the pattern on the paper covering this thin wood bandbox. Duodecagons alternate with diagonally-placed squares and scrolling arabesques fill in the spaces between these two free ornaments. A small twelve-petalled flower is placed inside the squares and the duodecagons are filled in with a squared-off design incorporating eight leafy forms. The tiny square in the center of this latter design itself encloses a four-petal rosette. Newspaper covering inside bottom of this box is copy of January 10, 1849 *Ohio Star*.

SIXTEEN-PETAL ROSETTE

This bandbox is the largest in the collection. The sixteen-petal design is block-printed on the paper in counter-changed colors, so that the background alternates in tone. The box is lined with newspapers from New Hampshire dating 1829. One of the news items is a release from Vienna dated February 15th telling of the death of His Holiness, Pope Leo the 12th, head of the Roman Catholic Church 1823–29.

Pink, white and blue on yellow background

22 x 17, 16" deep   No. 160   Circa 1830

EIGHT-PETAL ROSETTE

This thin wood bandbox is covered with a brilliant wallpaper in white, orange, red, and green varnish on a blue background. Two main motifs make up the pattern. Large eight-petal rosettes with alternating feathery petals and plain divisions fill in the spaces between the squared-off figure enclosing a smaller eight-petal rosette. A scrolling border encloses the figure and four six-petal rosettes embellish the four corners.

Undoubtedly this bandbox has been protected since it was new. One of the ways of keeping the paper fresh and bright was to make a draw-string cotton bag and place the bandbox inside the bag. The box could also be protected in this manner in transit, with the added advantage that the draw-string bag could be hoisted over the shoulder and carried by holding the string tie.

18½ x 13, 11½″ deep   No. 96   Circa 1835

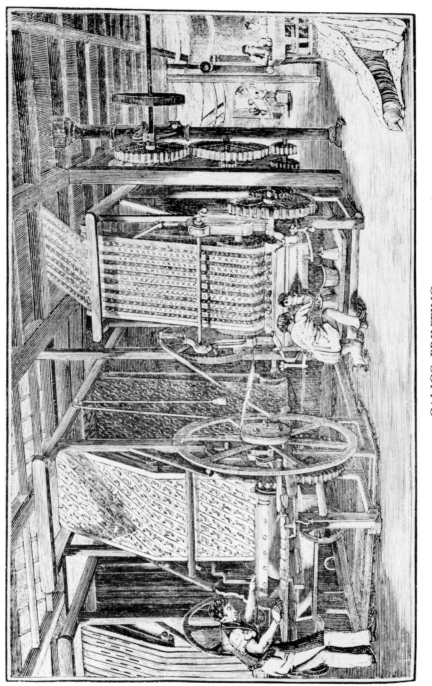

CALICO PRINTING

Engraving from "Memoir of Samuel Slater," by George S. White, published 1836

MACHINE-PRINTED PAPERS

Mechanics working in the calico-printing trade had realized for some time that the theory behind printing on rolls of paper and rolls of cloth was one and the same thing, but the development of a machine to print on long rolls of paper had to wait until an "endless papermaking machine" was perfected. A brevet d'invention for a papermaking machine had been taken out in 1799 by Louis Robert, a Frenchman and in 1805 an improved device to which two Englishmen, John Gamble and Bryan Donkin had contributed ideas was set up in Hertfordshire, England by H. & S. Fourdrinier, well-known wholesale stationers.

In place of the carved wood blocks, a rotary press with cylinders, cut in relief and run by hand was first tried out, but proved not too successful. In 1835 a one-color printing machine was invented in England by Bumstead and four years later the cylinders could print four colors. Although still hand-operated, two hundred rolls of paper per day could be run through this press. Credit for producing wallpaper by machine on a commercial scale, however, must belong to the firm of calico-printers, C. H. & E. Potter of Darwen, Lancashire, whose foreman, Walmsley Preston dismantled a calico-printing press and put it together again to make the prototype machine for printing wallpaper.

America received her first color printing machine from England in 1844. By this time the number of colors capable of being printed at once had multiplied to 59. Although occasionally block stamping was still resorted to for individual designs of special importance, the majority of wallpapers from that time on were "cylinder-printed by steam" and were available to all at a cheap price.

English paper-makers specialized in attempting to fill the enormous demand both at home and abroad for cheap papers and under the commercial system, their designs deteriorated in taste and artistic value. The French continued to concentrate on artistry and maintained a high quality ("in the matter of designs, a French maker will spend as many pounds as an English maker will spend pence"—*The Art Journal*, 1861), but their papers were so expensive that only the wealthy and discerning could afford or perhaps appreciate them.

In 1861, a group of English artists and craftsmen rebelled against the tasteless trends in the decorative arts and banded themselves into a guild type of organization known as "Morris, Marshall, Faulkner and Company, Fine Art Workmen in Painting, Carving, Furniture and Metals." Under their intense stewardship—("If it is not beautiful, it has no right to exist") —taste did improve somewhat, but the work of these artists never really reached the masses, for it was either too exclusive or too dear. By the time it had been "adapted" by the great factories whose object was to produce at a profit, sometimes the improvement in taste was so dim that it was barely discernible.

However, we are concerned with the period prior to this time, as the era of the bandbox co-incided with the period of the finest French hand-blocked wallpapers. Just as steam modified the making of wallpaper, so it also shifted the mode of travel. The steam train and the steam boat opened new horizons to travellers. Baggage rooms on the boats and baggage cars on the trains were large and capacious and the heavy brass-bound trunk which could withstand the rough handling of dock workers and baggage clerks became the accepted form of luggage. It was hail to the Saratoga trunk and farewell to the bandbox.

Diamonds

The lozenge-shaped panels with elliptical centers are outlined with disjointed four-sided lozenges made up of four wavy lines. Lined inside top and on bottom with *Rochester Daily Union & Advertiser* for December 8, 1863.

Blue, white and tan with red touches on beige background

7½ x 6, 5″ deep   No. 101   Circa 1865

Gothic Curves

Green, grey and red on ivory background

Round, 9½″ diameter, 6″ deep

No. 105   About 1865

Hazelton's Bonnet Box

According to Concord business directories, Mary J. and E. A. Hazelton were listed as milliners at the Rumford Block address in 1856. In the 1860–61 directory only Mary J. Hazelton's name appeared.

Tan, darker brown and electric blue on white background

13¾ x 12, 8½″ deep

No. 128

Circa 1856

Tropical Flowers

This box has been recovered several times and remnants of other papers are visible underneath the one here shown. The inside of the box has been lined with a printed wallpaper turned backwards and pasted down on the printed side.

Tan, black, green, blue and orange on green background

17 x 13, 10½" deep

No. 148

Mid-19th century

Ellipses and Floral Bouquets

This box has stripe design with alternating sprig branches and ellipses separating the stripes containing medallions of flowers enclosed by a rondelle of sheaves of wheat. Newspapers lining the box and on bottom date from 1847 and 1851.

An interesting tradecard pasted inside the cover of this box advertises the lozenges of I. P. Goldthwait, of Nashua, New Hampshire. According to Nashua business directories, the only I. P. Goldthwait recorded therein is one Ira P. Goldthwait

Orange, green, cream and red on gray background

Round, 8" diameter, 6" deep

No. 43

Circa 1851

who is described as a trader in the 1853 directory and as a peddler in subsequent directories up to and including 1874 after which his name does not re-appear. There is, however, a Calvin Goldthwait who is first listed as a sash maker and later as a confectioner. The Nashua City Engineer states that there was a "Shepard Block" located at 43–53 Factory Street, but after 1889 this too disappears. Neither Calvin nor Ira P Goldthwait was ever listed in the directories at the Factory Street address

Holly and Flowers

Thin wood box is covered with paper printed in red, black, pale yellow on a tan background.

15½ x 11, 10″ deep

No. 116

Mid-19th century

Pale green, white, gray and gold on blue field

Round, 7½″ diameter, 2¾″ deep

No. 42
Mid-19th century

Maple Leaves and Grapes

The design of foliage, flowers and fruits has been dotted with gold.

All-over Floral

This bandbox was originally covered with a floral paper of pink, red and green varnish on a blue ground. The inside was lined with an 1834 newspaper. Later it was repapered with a late 19th century paper and relined with a *Boston Herald* newspaper of 1883.

The modern paper: yellow, fuchsia, black, white and gold dots on a grey background

9½ x 7½, 4½″ deep

No. 40   Late 19th century

Interlacing Foliage Vines

This box is made of layers of old newspapers pasted and pressed together. Covered with machine-printed wallpaper in green and red on a glazed white background. The inside rim of the cover has been reinforced with newspapers, one of which has date of 1841.

11 x 8, 6½″ deep

No. 162   Mid-19th century

Diamonds in Ogival Frames

The geometrical paper covering this box has an almost masculine appeal to it, but the box was used for "fringe" and is so labelled in ink on the cover. It is lined with a bright yellow broadside advertising the Consolidated Lottery, decided by the drawing of the Delaware State Lottery, to be drawn at Wilmington, Delaware March 22, 1855 with capital prize of $13,000. Lotteries played an important part in the development of all of the States. The Dutch used them as early as 1655 in New York to raise money for poor relief and King's College, now Columbia was begun with funds raised by lotteries held between 1747 and 1754. In Vermont many of the covered bridges were built with money raised in this manner.

Yellow, brown and white on pale green field

Round, 9″ diameter, 5″ deep

No. 41   Circa 1855

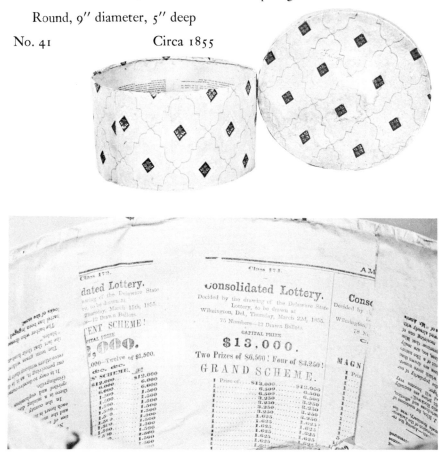

Joseph Schwab Hat Box

This light cardboard box is covered with wallpaper in tan and brown with sprigs of flowers outlined with a thin red line. Top is a machine printed wallpaper in leaf design in tan and blue; blue paper reinforces the rim.

The tradecard of Joseph Schwab pasted to the side of the box advertised laces, ribbons, fringes, trimmings, embroideries, hoisery, gloves, silk, velvet, satin, straw and fancy bonnets, dress-caps, &c. as well as cloaks, mantillas and corsets. "Country merchants supplied at lowest New York prices. Bonnets, dress-caps and head-dresses, made to order."

Joseph Schwab was located in Hartford, Connecticut in 1861, 1862 and 1863. His name does not appear after that date in business directories.

14 x 11, 9½″ deep

No. 109   Circa 1861–63

Detached Floral Sprays

This box when it was given to the museum contained a straw bonnet which was worn by Mrs. Hannah Ballard Greene, who lived in Carmel, New York.

Gift of Mrs. J. I. Hoffecker, New Canaan, Conn.

Green, brown, gray and tan and gold on white background

10 x 8, 6″ deep   No. 157   Mid-19th Century

TRANSPORTATION
DESIGNS

Coach Scene

Who is she that is growing up to the good fortune of riding in a coach and two? She is the girl who rises with the rising day; whose hands and face are made clean; whose hair is cleared of snarly locks and neatly rolled in papers; and whose clothes are clean and whole, though never gay. She who loves her book, her school, the truth and her parents, and also the path of peace and virtue. I now see her through the window of the carriage, and I hear her say:

What though I ride in a coach and pair
And in dress and food like a princess fare;
I'll not be proud like the haughty Moor;
Nor stop my ear at the cry of the poor.

The De Witt Clinton Primer, published 1830

This coach scene appears three times in the museum collection—on a double-printed design bandbox (along with "Volunteer Fireman," see page 182): on a full length panel which is a steamed-open bandbox mounted on wood board; and on a fragment, showing a single motif of the coach scene. In all cases the block printing is in red, white and green varnish on a blue background.

21 x 17, 14" deep   Box No. 132

56 x 13"   Panel No. 2

Nancy McClelland, Inc. of New York has reproduced this paper in lilac, white and olive green on ochre ground and a sample has been photographed to show the design with greater clarity.

Modern reproduced design

Gift of Hobe Erwin, New York

21 x 13"   Panel Fragment No. 45

American Index of Design rendering of a privately owned bandbox in Connecticut. Rendered by Martin Partyka.

Coaching Print

Now I wish I had retained one half of the coaching songs, anecdotes and other matters, which might have interested or amused those who still care about coaching. I remember a few lines of a coaching song written by an old friend in 1835:

> Some people delight in the sports of the turf,
>   Whilst others love only the chase;
> But to me the delight of all others is
>   A coach that can go the pace.
> There are some too for whom the sea has its charms,
>   And who sing of it night and morn,
> But give me a coach with its rattling bars,
>   And a guard who can blow his horn.
>
> How the girls all doat on the sight of a coach,
>   And the dragsman's curly locks,
> As he rattles along with eleven and four
>   And a petticoat on the box;
> His box is his home, his teams are his pride,
>   And he ne'er looks downcast or forlorn;
> And he lists to the musical sound of the bars,
>   And a blast on the old mail horn.

Amateur Reminiscences of Old Coaching Days by the Duke of Somerset, written about 1885.

These few lines aptly describe the scene appearing on the bandbox cover here pictured. Time and exposure have darkened the colors so that

it is now dim and clouded. However, this scene is one on file at the National Gallery of Art, Washington, D. C. in its Index of American Design. Their portrayal of the print is reproduced above.

Pink, white and dark varnish on blue field

19 x 15"   Top to box No. 23

Circa 1835

Windmill Railroad

The first railroad was literally a road of two rails extending three miles from the Quincy, Massachusetts granite quarries to the bridge on the Neponset River. Built to haul the blocks of granite to erect the Bunker Hill Monument, the rolling stock consisted of four wooden cars with wooden wheels. It was opened in October of 1826 and newspapers of the day reported that in the presence of a number of gentlemen who take an interest in such experiments, a quantity of stone weighing 16 tons was loaded on three wagons (themselves together weighing five tons) and the total load of 21 tons "was moved with ease, by a single horse" down the gradual three-mile decline. The horse then returned the empty wagons "in a fast walk after the starting of the load, which required some exertion." This road never carried passengers.

Later on other companies laid out railroads, some for passenger service and some for freight traffic, but for some years, the motive power continued to be animal power. In fact the Baltimore and Ohio system in the beginning was set up to allow individuals to use the railroad by furnishing their own horses and flanged-wheel wagons. The company was to receive a toll for the privilege of using its rails.

The wallpaper cover on this bandbox shows a horse drawing three cars loaded with freight—baled cotton, logs, and what appear to be huge blocks of stone. In the background is a windmill and printed on the box is the legend: "Windmill Rail Road."

19 x 15, 11¾" deep   No. 81   Circa 1830

Thin wood box, covered with paper printed in pink, white and olive-green
varnish on yellow field

Gift of Mr. Titus Geesey, Wilmington, Delaware

Steam Locomotive

Experiments in energy-producing methods for hauling trains of cars on the double rails ranged over a wide field in the first few years of the history of railroads. In addition to experiments with horse-drawn locomotion, a southern railroad tested a square-rigged sail mounted to its passenger car. A horse-powered treadmill car "The Flying Dutchman" was investigated in 1830, but this too proved a poor speculation.

The Delaware & Hudson Canal Company line imported in 1829 from England a steam locomotive. After its arrival in America it was found to weigh seven tons. Unfortunately this was an overload on the then-existing track and trestle in Pennsylvania where it was intended for use and it was relegated to stationary service. Eventually it was dismantled.

Peter Cooper's "Tom Thumb" proved a much better venture. Built at a local iron works for the Baltimore & Ohio railroad, it proved itself in a famous race with an exceedingly fast gray horse. Although the race was lost, it demonstrated it could pull a load of forty people at ten miles an hour. It was apparent to all that the steam railroad had come to stay, and its reign did, in fact, last for more than a century.

The paper covering this bandbox shows a steam locomotive, resembling the one made in England by George Stephenson and used in 1835 to pull the first train on the Boston & Lowell line. The car immediately after the locomotive is for passengers, but experience soon disclosed the best place for the passenger car was at the end of the train—there was less likelihood of sparks from the engine igniting the gowns worn by the ladies. The cattle car is next in line and last is a flat car loaded with logs.

Gift of Mrs. Katharine Prentis Murphy, New York
Pink, white, yellow and green varnish on blue field
13½ x 13¼"   19 x 15, 12½" deep

Fragment panel No. 36   No. 23   Circa 1835

Sailing Ship

At the close of the Revolution, shipping merchants in the young United States found themselves stripped of their hard-wrung wealth, and not knowing how to make use of their new-found peace. Many of the whaling fleet had been destroyed; Congress had little authority and consequently failed to protect the new merchant fleet that was slowly and painfully being pieced together by a few courageous shipowners and sailors. A deep depression had settled down over the northern maritime states; industry was at a standstill. American ships had to "seek their own fair winds." They were not too long in finding them.

In 1784 the rechristened privateer of 360 tons burthen *Empress of China* set out on the trip around the Cape of Good Hope and across the Indian Ocean to Canton. Fifteen months later Capt. Samuel Shaw sailed into New York harbor with a profit of $30,000 for his backers. The race was on! At first our ships took corn, salt fish, barrel staves, shingles and genseng root; later the cargo was fur, silver dollars, candles, glass lanterns and chandeliers. They brought home from the Orient their fabled silks and tea and from the famed Spice Islands, pepper and other piquant seasonings,

---

Red, white and green varnish on blue field	Pink, white and amber varnish on yellow background
17 x 13½" Top to Box No. 3	17 x 14" Top No. 22
Circa 1835	Circa 1835

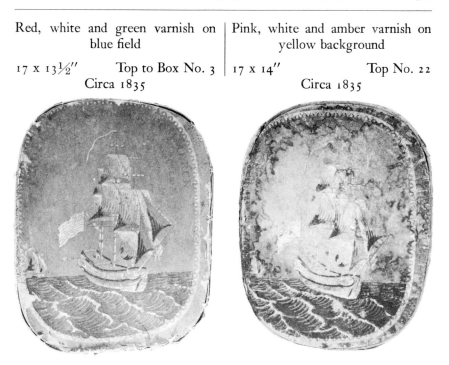

ivory, mother-of-pearl, lacquered tables, screens, boxes and the sought-after china ware.

Even Congress at last gave actual support to shipping with an Act providing a 10 per cent discount on import duties on cargoes carried in American ships. However, under the provisions of the Peace Establishment Act of 1801, Congress decided to disband the fleet specifically built "to defend the merchant marine." In the Mediterranean the Barbary pirates flourished and America, like other nations throughout the world, paid the annual protection money or "tribute" demanded by the Dey of Algiers. In the so-called Algerine War of 1815, Stephen Decatur in a daring exploit forced the Dey to sign a treaty giving up the tribute. Commerce with foreign countries could now be carried on in a climate free from fear. The legend "Prosperity to Our Commerce and Manufacturers," which though faded is still visible on the hat box covers illustrated, was now an assurance, rather than a hope.

Combination Steam and Full-rigged Sailing Ship

. . . The invention of the steam engine, simple in its construction, but wonderful in its effects and infinite in its application stands unrivalled, as a monument of human ingenuity and enterprise. No example of this truth can be cited which will call up such thrilling sensations in the bosom of an American, as the application of steam to navigation. An interesting train of reflections crowd upon the imagination at the mere mention of the subject. The beautiful and uniform movements of the steam engine, urging onward with unsurpassing speed the numerous boats scattered over the smooth waters of the Hudson, the Delaware, the Connecticut, and Ohio, successfully resisting the united efforts of wind and tide. . . . the effect which has been produced upon the settlement and civilization of our western territories—the rude log huts disappearing along the banks of the Mississippi—the wild prairies covered with luxuriant vegetation—cities, towns and villages rising, as if by magic—the peaceful lowing of the cattle in the fields, instead of the shrill war-whoop resounding through the forest; all combine to produce a noble representation of the effect of the cultivation of the arts and sciences upon civilization. And when we consider, that to the genius, perseverance and enterprise of one of our own countrymen, we are indebted for this improvement of our western wilds, we cannot fail to respond with fervor to the exclamation of the patriot, "This is my own, my native land."

By Junius, Boston, Jan. 14, 1834, published in the *Young Mechanic*, conducted by an association of practical mechanics, devoted to Mathematics, Natural Philosophy, Chemistry, The Arts, Manufacturers, Internal Improvements, etc.

Even before a transatlantic crossing completely under steam had been attempted, several endeavors had been made to conquer this ocean in a combination steam-and-sailing vessel. The first of these was in 1819 when Capt. Moses Rogers of New London, Connecticut essayed the trip in such a boat with paddle wheels that could be folded up like a fan and taken aboard. The *Savannah* actually reached Liverpool, but the paddlewheels had been used for only 80 hours of the crossing which consumed 29 days. The little Dutch navy vessel, the *Curacao* left Holland in April of 1827 and arrived in the Dutch West Indies less than a month later, having used steam practically all the way. The third transatlantic steamship was the Canadian *Royal William*, but she was badly damaged by a heavy gale during her attempted crossing six years later.

The scene was set, but it was not until 1838 that two ships almost simultaneously entered the New York harbor, both under steam and with their sails completely furled. See page 125 for the story of this memorable event.

Red, white and yellow varnish on
blue background

16 x 13, 11″ deep

No. 129

Circa 1835

Bandbox steamed open and faded fragments mounted on panel. Identical design but printed in orange, white and amber varnish on mauve field

38 x 14″   Panel No. 21   Circa 1835

Steamships *Great Western* and *British Queen*

Block printed on one of the bandbox covers in the museum collection is the steamship *British Queen*. Pasted inside the cover of the tiny bandbox shown on page 64 is a water color of the steamer *Great Western* built in Britain to capture the prestige prize of inaugurating steam service from England to New York. Experts had maintained that steamboats would require far too much wood or coal to run their engines across the Atlantic, and even as late as 1835, the English Association for Advancement of Science members were warned that schemes for crossing the Atlantic by steam were "perfectly chimerical and they might as well talk of making a voyage from New York to the moon."

Nevertheless at least two British companies worked feverishly to complete the ship that would be the first to make the trip a reality. While the

Pink and chalky white with touches of amber varnish printed on medium blue background

14 x 10½″

Top No. 19

Circa 1841

Hand-painted water color pasted inside cover to box

No. 15

6 x 4″

Circa 1838

British Queen and the *Great Western* were abuilding, a small sidewheeler called the *Sirius* was chartered and embarked for America. The *Great Western* left four days later, but her captain hoped to overtake the slower vessel and arrive in New York first. Trouble dogged the ship from the start. Even before she left port, a fire broke out in the steam chests, one of the company directors fell off a ladder, some of the stokers deserted and most of the passengers cancelled. Still the *Great Western* cut down the lead of the *Sirius* from four days to one. At the last moment the *Sirius* nosed into a mud bank at Sandy Hook and had to wait until high tide the following day so that even as she entered the harbor there was seen over Governors Island "a dense, black cloud of smoke spreading itself upwards and betokening another arrival. . . . the steamship *Great Western* . . . rakish, cool, reckless, fierce—her sails all furled and the engines at their topmost speed."

Newspaper accounts echoed the excitement of that memorable April 23, 1838. Announcement of the arrivals was carried by telegraph and brought thousands to every point of view upon the water side—boats too, in shoals, were out to welcome her. At the Battery "myriads seemed collected, boats had gathered in countless confusion, flags flying, guns firing—it seemed as though they would never have done."

This *British Queen* box top was manufactured by William Varnum and his trade card appears pasted inside. Business directories first list him at this address in 1841. The listings run through 1847 and do not appear thereafter.

Paddlewheel Steamboat

The innumerable steam boats, which are the stage coaches and fly waggons of this land of lakes and rivers

commented the English Mrs. Trollope in her 1832 book on the "Domestic Manners of the Americans"

are totally unlike any I had seen in Europe, and greatly superior to them. . . . The room to which the double line of windows belongs is a very handsome apartment; before each window a neat little cot is arranged in such a manner as to give its drapery the air of a window curtain. This room is called the gentlemen's cabin, and their exclusive right to it is somewhat uncourteously insisted upon. The breakfast, dinner and supper are laid in this apartment, and the lady passengers are permitted to take their meals there. . . . We found the room destined for the use of the ladies dismal enough, as its only windows were below the stern gallery; but both this and the gentlemen's cabin were handsomely fitted up and the latter well carpeted; but oh! that carpet! I will not, I may not describe its condition. . . . I would infinitely prefer sharing the apartment of a party of well-conditioned pigs to the being confined to its cabin.

Charles Dickens, writing in 1842 had this to say in his *American Notes:*

There is one American boat—the vessel which carried us on Lake Champlain . . . which I praise very highly, but no more than it deserves. The steamboat which is called the *Burlington* is a perfectly exquisite achievement of neatness, elegance and order. The decks are drawingrooms; the cabins are boudoirs, choicely furnished and adorned with prints, pictures, and musical instruments; every nook and corner of the vessel is a perfect curiosity of graceful comfort and beautiful contrivance.

Another foreign visitor—this time Sir James Lucuzthn, Lord Provost of Glasgow, Scotland acclaimed this same ship:

We went on board the *Burlington* one of the most splendid and commodious of steam vessels. . . . The interior decorations are so truly splendid that you might fancy yourself in the drawing room of a ducal palace. The cleanliness of the vessel is the admiration of all strangers. There is no unpleasant shouting or noise. . . . The arrangements at meals are excellent and the greatest attention paid to the passengers by the stewards, who are numerous and all dressed in neat, clean, fancy uniforms.

The steamboat block-printed on the paper covering this bandbox is of an early type. The bandbox itself is one of the most interesting in the collection. On the other side of the box is the beaver shown on page 40 and on the top the arrangement of hats and caps depicted on page 21.

Black, blue and green on pale green background with blue dots filling the intermediate spaces between motifs

12½ x 9½, 8″ deep

No. 49

Circa 1835

Providence River

Featured on this bandbox is a view showing an American steamboat and also a fully rigged sailing ship. In background is a church, tree and two small ships.

Blue and green on yellow background

20 x 16, 14″ deep

No. 144   Circa 1835

The section through which Providence River flows was settled by the Puritan minister, Roger Williams in 1636. He secured title to the land from friendly Narragansett Indians and named his settlement in honor and gratitude for God's merciful Providence. The town in 1833 was described in the *Traveller's Guide through the Middle and Northern States:*

> built on both sides of the river, across which is an elegant bridge; and is one of the most wealthy and enterprising places in the union. Besides a great variety of extensive manufacturing establishments, it contains a court house, town house, market, hospital, 7 banks, a college, 3 academies and several churches; and its population is not far from 18,000.

The Blackstone Canal terminated at Providence and steamboats left six times weekly for New York—in 1833 the fare was six dollars. Three times per week stages left for Norwich and Middletown and daily to Hartford. The Providence stage for New London, 59 miles distant, connected with a steamboat line for New York and residents proudly announced that the railroad from Providence to Stonington, Connecticut, then abuilding, when completed would give an uninterrupted steamboat and railroad communication between Boston and New York.

In the 18th century the City of Providence owed its prosperity to the fact that it was a port of entry and an important harbor. During the 19th century, owing to its many streams and rivers rushing with precipitous falls, Providence maintained its position during the Industrial Revolution because of its water power available for manufacturing. It became widely known as a center for silverware, jewelry, machine tools, hardware, watches, oil products and textiles.

Walking Beam Sidewheeler

The castle-like building flying the American flag and the bridge depicted on this bandbox have not been identified, but the steamboat is one of the walking-beam sidewheelers with covered paddle box. On the other side of the box, additional buildings are depicted and another means of transportation—a boat with one man rowing and the other passenger propelling the boat with a pole.

The manuscript notation on the box shows that it once belonged to Sophia Van Doren. It was found in New Jersey.

In 1832, Mrs. Trollope, the indefatigable English traveller described her trip on one of the Hudson River steamboats:

> About thirty miles further is Hyde Park . . . here the misty summit of the distant Kaatskill begins to form the outline of the landscape; it is hardly possible to imagine anything more beautiful than this place. We passed a day there with great enjoyment; and the following morning set forward again in one of those grand floating hotels called steamboats. Either on this day or the one before we had two hundred cabin passengers on board, and they all sat down together to a table spread abundantly and with considerable elegance. A continual succession of gentlemen's seats (country residences), many of them extremely handsome, borders the river to Albany.

Pink and white with amber varnish on yellow background

16 x 13, 11″ deep   No. 27   About 1835

American Steamboat

THE STEAMBOAT ON TRIAL

. . . When a large steamboat is built, with the intention of having her employed upon the waters of a great river, she must be proved before put to service. . . . It is not certain that her machinery will work at all, there may be some flaw in the iron or an imperfection in some part of the workmanship, which will prevent the motion of her wheels. . . . The engineer cautiously builds a fire under her boiler; he watches with eager interest the rising of the steam-gage, and scrutinizes every part of the machinery, as it gradually comes under the control of the tremendous power which he is cautiously applying. With what interest does he observe the first stroke of the ponderous piston! And when at length, the fastenings of the boat are let go, and the motion is communicated to the wheels, and the mighty mass slowly moves away from the wharf, how deep and eager an interest does he feel in all her movements, and in every indication he can discover of her future success. . . . He scrutinizes the action of every lever and the friction of every joint; here he oils a bearing, there he tightens a nut; one part of the machinery has too much play and he confines it; another too much friction and he loosens it; now he stops the engine, now reverses her motion and again sends the boat forward in her course.

. . . . And what are its results? Why after this course has been thoroughly and faithfully pursued, this floating palace receives upon her broad deck and in her carpeted and curtained cabins her four or five hundred passengers who pour in, in one long procession of happy groups, over the bridge of planks; father and son, mother and children, young husband and wife—all with implicit confidence trusting themselves and their dearest interest to her power.

See her as she sails away—how beautiful and yet how powerful are all her motions! That beam glides up and down gently and smoothly in its grooves, and yet gentle as it seems, hundreds of horses could not hold it still; there is no apparent violence, but every movement is withal most irresistible power. How graceful is her form, and yet how mighty is the momentum with which she presses on her way. Loaded with life and herself the very symbol of life and power she seems something ethereal—unreal, which, ere we look again will have vanished away.

Lesson 96 of *The Second Class Reader* designed for the use of the middle class of schools in the United States, by B. D. Emerson, Boston 1833.

On both sides and on the top of the box is block printed an American steamboat set off by chalky white scrolls. Separating the steamboats are nautical trophies—decorative elements having to do with the sea—in this case a twisted line or rope fouling an anchor. This box has the words "Fashionable Hats Caps Gloves Umbrellas" printed around the rim of the cover. John C. and Charles Cook, manufacturers of the bandbox shown on page 22, were also the makers of this box. They were located at the 220 Washington Street, Boston address from 1831 through 1836.

Orange, white and black on deep ultramarine blue field

11 x 9, 9" deep   No. 48   Circa 1835

JOHN C. & CHARLES COOK,
IMPORTERS AND MANUFACTURERS OF
PAPER HANGINGS,
BORDERS AND CHIMNEY BOARD PRINTS.

ALSO MANUFACTURE
HAT and BONNET BOXES by the DOZEN or HUNDRED,
AT REDUCED PRICES.

STORE 220 WASHINGTON STREET,
BOSTON.

Erie Canal

ALSO CALLED "GRAND CANAL"

As early as 1760, men of vision had foreseen the desirability of the construction of a continuous waterway linking the Great Lakes to the Atlantic Ocean if our country was to develop the vast western portion. The Revolution intervened, but through the efforts of Philip Schuyler a beginning had been made by 1796 when it became possible for boats of 16 tons to pass through a canal linking Schenectady to Lake Ontario.

The success of this early channel led to the digging of the Grand Canal, as the project was designated in the 1812 report published by the Inland Navigation Commission of New York state. This waterway, later named the Erie Canal, connected the straggling towns of Buffalo on Lake Erie to Albany on the Hudson, and opened a water route from the Lakes to the Atlantic Ocean.

The canal was begun in 1817 and the views on the hat boxes here illustrated depict the scene at Little Falls, a town on the Mohawk River, not far from Utica. The arched bridge in the background was called the Aqueduct Bridge. This wall of masonry that lifted the canal over the Mohawk was 30 feet high and was regarded as one of the engineering marvels of the century. The bridge with its three arches was built of granite.

Both the eastern and western portions of the canal presented their own specific construction difficulties. The deep cuts and series of locks con-

Blue and white with amber varnish on faded yellow background

11 x 10½"

Panel No. 38

Circa 1830

structed at Lockport on the western portion vied with the 16 great piers crossing the Mohawk River on the eastern end. Where the Mohawk was recrossed a few miles further on, an even longer aqueduct resting on 26 piers was erected.

At Troy the Champlain Canal coming down from the North joined the Erie and together they headed for Albany. Here, 363 miles by its course from Buffalo the canals entered the Hudson, with deep water to the open sea. The dream of a century had come true. In October of 1825 a keg of water from Lake Erie was poured into the Atlantic Ocean, symbolizing the merging of the geographic limits of our country. Even more significant to the development of America was the fact that freight rates between New York and Buffalo promptly dropped from one hundred dollars to eight dollars per ton and the time required for shipment likewise fell from six weeks to ten days.

Many problems yet remained to solve, however. The passage of the boats through the canals was sufficient to raise a wave which washed out the banks on either side of the canal. The canal boats travelled at a speed of four miles per hour and the *Boston Mechanic and Journal of the Useful Arts and Sciences* for April 1835 suggested the "Fly Boats" operating on one of the British canals should be investigated. Because these boats travelled at a speed of ten miles per hour, it was felt that the wake would not damage the banks of the Erie Canal as badly. The boats themselves were from 70 to 90 feet long and from six to seven feet wide. Hulls were of sheet iron plates and bottoms flat, or nearly so. Inside were seats on either side, furnished with cushions and with passageway between. The boats were covered with gay painted awnings stretched over wooden hoops and lined with glazed cotton. Cost of the boat in England amounted to about $550 and the whole expense of running four trips or 48 miles on an English canal, including "horses, attendants, interest and twenty per cent for a reserved fund to replace boats, horses and other incidental expenses" amounted to about $2,100 per annum or twenty-two cents per mile. The engraving here included shows the plan of the Fly Boats in detail and is taken from the *Boston Mechanic*.

Completion of the Erie Canal had its international implications and its prestige value to America was immeasurable. It brought the State of New York to the attention of the civilized world and was declared in Europe to be the greatest accomplishment of the new American nation. "New York has built the longest canal in the world in the least time, with the least experience, for the least money and to the greatest public benefit." Time has indeed proved this encomium was entirely deserved.

The two bandboxes, the top and fragment of wallpaper here shown all seem to have been adapted from the print entitled "View of the Aqueduct Bridge at Little Falls" appearing in the 1825 *Memoir Prepared for the Celebration of the Completion of the New York Canals* by Cadwallader D. Colden.

Red, white and green varnish on green background faded to blue

Round, 19½″ diameter 17″ deep   No. 6   Circa 1830

Pink, white and amber varnish on yellow background	Pink, white and green varnish on cream background
17 x 14, 11″ deep	15 x 11″ Top of box No. 62
No. 127 Circa 1830	Circa 1830

Port of Buffalo

This hat box bears the legend "Port of Buffaloe on Lake Erie," and a manuscript tag on the cover shows that at one time it belonged to Mrs. Phebe Cook of East Greene, Rhode Island.

White, pink and brown varnish on creamy yellow field

17½ x 14, 11″ deep   No. 9   Circa 1835

Capt. Marryat, an Englishman touring this country in the 1830's had this to say of Buffalo:

It is one of the wonders of America. It is hardly to be credited that such a beautiful city could have risen up in the wilderness in so short a period. In the year 1814 it was burnt down, being then only a village; only one house left standing, and now it is a city with 25,000 inhabitants. (Today it is the second largest city in New York State with a population in 1950 of 580,132 persons). The Americans are very judicious in planning their new towns; the streets are laid out so wide that there will never be any occasion to pull down to widen and improve, as we do in England. The City of Buffalo is remarkably well built; all the houses in the principal streets are lofty and substantial and are either of brick or granite. The main street is wider and the stores handsomer, than the majority of those in New York. It has five or six very fine churches, a handsome theatre, town hall and market and three or four hotels, one of which is superior to most others in America; and to these we must add a fine stone pier, with a lighthouse and a harbour full of shipping and magnificent steamboats. It is almost incomprehensible that all this should have been accomplished since the year 1814. And what has occasioned this springing up of a city in so short a time as to remind one of Aladdin's magic Palace?—The Erie Canal, which here joins the Hudson River with the Lake passing through the centre of the most populous and fertile states.

Clayton's Ascent

This bandbox commemorates the aerostation experiences of Richard Clayton, a young Englishman who in the early 1830's joined the westward movement after his arrival in America. Settling in Cincinnati in 1834 he practiced his trade of clock and watchmaking and enjoyed a hobby of ballooning. A record was established in his spectacular ascent from the Cincinnati Amphitheatre in April of 1835 and his 350 mile voyage into Munroe County, Virginia.

Red, white and blue field   Red and white on yellow field

15 x 12, 10″ deep   Top to box No. 138

No. 2   About 1835

Ballooning excited a remarkable amount of interest among all classes and great fear among the uneducated. We have an account of the 18th century French peasants who watched the first unmanned balloon land, unheralded, near the village of Gonesse. With their pitchforks they stabbed at the 40 pound taffeta monster plastered over with an elastic gum and filled with inflammable air. As the hydrogen hissed out they fell upon it and beat it to death.

As a matter of record, the Soviets insist that in 1731 a Russian trapped smoke in a bag and rode it "as high as a birch tree." History, however, has credited Stephen and Joseph de Montgolfier, Frenchmen, with the invention of the first successful balloon. The brothers, paper manufacturers, raised their paper balloon or Montgolfière by rarified air. They had tried hydrogen gas, but without success, for it escaped through the pores of their paper. The skin of this first gas balloon was elaborately decorated by Reveillon, the famous 18th century wallpaper manufacturer and the flight

Red, white and pale green varnish on blue

22 x 14″   Top No. 2   About 1835

itself took place in the garden of "Folie Titon"—which was the name of his enormous factory. The first successful balloon was 110 feet in circumference and was made of coarse linen lined with paper. Shortly thereafter the Montgolfiers sent up a balloon with a car in which they had placed a sheep, a cock and a duck. The first human ascended in a balloon firmly attached to the ground by means of a rope, but soon thereafter he and a friend performed the hazardous and until then untried experiment of navigating the air in a Montgolfière. The machine's ascent was estimated at three thousand feet and it travelled horizontally for about 20 to 25 minutes. The following month a voyage of an hour and three-quarters was made; in that time the balloon had travelled 25 miles from Paris. Wings, a rudder and a parachute were added to the balloon next, but the rudder proved useless in controlling the movements. However, a dog was successfully parachuted to the ground and landed safely.

One cannot help comparing the time scheduling of events having to do with the early history of ballooning and the satellite programs now going on in America and elsewhere. This comparison remains valid, for balloons soon came to be regarded as important military machines for making reconnaissances. One was distributed during the French Revolution to each of the Republican Armies, and in 1794, a body of troops was raised in France "for the purpose of reconnoitering the position of the enemy by the air of balloons." The air ships were manned by two officers who communicated by flags and slips of paper the results of their observations to the troops beneath them. This experiment was soon abandoned, but by 1804, under the auspices of the French government, the first ascent for purely scientific objects was made. Instruments were furnished for experimenting upon the "density, temperature, humidity and electricity of the air at different elevations, and also upon the phenomena of magnetism and galvanism, that might be developed." A flask was developed so that air from the highest elevation could be brought to earth for analysis.

Even as late as 1857, the *American Cyclopaedia* maintained that although balloons might be used to some extent for passing from one part of the country to another, still "man has yet to discover some new principles that shall give him a partial control over the elements . . . before he can apply to any important purpose the power he possesses of rising into the air."

ROMANTIC AND NEO-CLASSICAL DESIGNS

Garden Tempiettos and Fountains

With the discovery of the ancient Italian cities of Herculaneum and Pompeii in the middle of the 18th century and the publication of several books of designs from the wall paintings there, an intense interest in all things classical developed in the design field.

The readers of Godey's *Lady Book* for April 1835 were treated to a first-hand account by a returning traveller:

Pompeii was anciently a walled city of about two miles in circumference, originally washed by the sea, though it is now a mile distant. It is about six or seven miles from the top of Vesuvius, and a little farther from Mount Somma, which in the year 79 of our era, poured upon Pompeii ashes, hot water, and pumice stones, and upon Herculaneum solid lava, burying both for seventeen centuries. I walked the streets of Pompeii, which was not even discovered until 1750, and which now stands disinterred in melancholy grandeur, the city of resurrection. I saw her disinterred temples, theatres, villas, prisons, and tombs. I saw yet standing the abode of their deities, or rather of the craft of the priesthood of Pompeii. The splendid house of Diomed, the spacious and sumptuous city baths, and the richly ornamented fountains are here. The pavement is deeply worn by the wheels of carriages, showing the great antiquity of Pompeii. The sleep of seventeen centuries is broken, but the light of life dawns not again on this ancient city.

Yellow, pink and amber varnish on blue background

17 x 14"   Top No. 17

Circa 1835

Edward Bulwer Lytton's *Last Days of Pompeii* was written at Naples during the winter of 1832–33 and upon its publication became a best seller. Travellers included a trip to the "City of the Dead" in all the Grand Tours and upon returning to their own homes evoked the past by building anew their own version of the ancient ruins in Italy. "Ruins" became the fashion, and no formal garden was complete without its decaying and demolished temple or fountain.

Pink, white and amber varnish on yellow field

20 x 15, 13½" deep   Box No. 31   19 x 15"   Top No. 16

Circa 1835

Quadriga Filled with Flowers

The chariot depicted on this box is a quadriga and was meant to be drawn by four horses abreast. It is to be found on ancient coins and in Roman antiquity.

The discovery in 1748 of the lava-covered ruins in Pompeii and Herculaneum generated interest in classical motifs and the vogue for classical design continued in America until well into the 19th century.

The completion of Monticello in 1809 by Thomas Jefferson in Charlottesville, Virginia and his architectural designs for the University of Virginia (opened in 1825) revived interest in classical buildings and commenced the period we now know as Greek Revival. This time interval likewise coincided with the settlement of large portions of our nation—both to the west and to the south. It is no surprise that the civic buildings,

Rose, white and green varnish on ultramarine field

49 x 11″   Panel No. 9   Circa 1830

court houses, capitols and other large public edifices in these newly established communities drew inspiration from the Greek and Roman Classical
Orders.

Another factor was also at work. America has so recently acquired her
own freedom from a dominating oppressor, that when the Greek War of
Independence commenced in 1821, an overwhelming sentiment in favor of
Greece developed. This occurred not only in America, however, but in
European countries also. The rebellion, under the leadership of the patriot
Demetrios Ypsilanti, a member of a distinguished family, was not success-
ful at first, but sympathetic citizens of other countries contributed not only
financial aid, but many volunteered and served with the Greek forces.

In 1826 Russia and England agreed to mediate between the Greeks and
Turkey. The following year, the Greek political factions set aside their
bitter internal rivalries long enough to elect a president and that same year
France joined with England and Russia in demanding an armistice. When
Turkey refused, allied fleets attacked and defeated the opposing fleet.
Turkey accepted the treaty of Adrianople and recognized Greece as an
autonomous principality. In 1832 Greece obtained recognition by the
European powers of its complete independence, but not before they had
fought a civil war which lasted for one year.

Americans paid homage to the brave Greek peoples in our own way.
New cities established during these years took names honoring ancient

Pink, white and dark
varnish on blue field

20 x 17, 12″ deep

No. 64

Circa 1830

Greek cities. The patriot Ypsilanti lives forever in the names of the cities of Georgia, North Dakota and Michigan which perpetuate the alien aggregation of consonants in his surname. Ithaca is the designation of a large city in New York state, but Michigan, Nebraska, Ohio and Wisconsin all have their own Ithacas. Three states, California, Kentucky and Washington have honored Olympia. Marathon is located in Florida, Iowa, New York, Ohio, Wisconsin and Texas. Perhaps the most popular of all the ancient cities so honored is Syracuse. Indiana, Kansas, Missouri, Nebraska, Ohio, South Carolina and Utah, as well as New York have chosen this appellation for a city within their borders.

Classical Architecture

Characteristics of the Greek and Roman Classical Orders included restraint, harmony of parts and a perfection of proportion. Their buildings were often rectangular with an overhanging, low-pitched, peaked roof supported by a row of slightly tapered fluted pillars. The unidentified building illustrated on this bandbox paper answers this description admirably with its 12 columns and 5 balanced doors. Research has failed to establish whether it is an actual building or an adaptation of the Palais Bourbon which is one of the buildings included in "Les Monuments de Paris." This scenic wall paper, designed by Brock, was printed by Dufour and Leroy in 1814 or 1815 in France. The Palais Bourbon, now the seat of the French National Assembly, also presents a facade with 12 columns, 5 doors and a similar pediment—that ornamented triangular space or low gable over the front of the building. Their pediment is filled with sculptured relief of a figure in a chariot being pulled by two horses, with cherubs and angels hovering in front and behind the vehicle.

Pink, white and green varnish on a blue field
Bandbox steamed open and mounted on a panel

50 x 11″ Panel No. 17   Circa 1830

"Monuments of Paris" was one of the most popular papers ever issued by Joseph Dufour. Nancy McClelland in her book on *Historic Wallpapers* lists 14 known examples of this paper in America. In 1817 James H. Foster of Boston advertised that he had just received some rich paper hangings, among them "Setts of Monuments of Paris, a very elegant hanging." At the time of its first edition, the set sold in France for 50 francs and consisted of 30 strips in color, formed of small sheets glued together. All the important buildings of Paris were shown as occupying the banks of the River Seine. The foreground featured pastoral scenes of people engaged in many activities—hunting, fishing and bathing on the banks of the river. Examples of this paper are known in houses located in Massachusetts, New Hampshire, Virginia, Maine, South Carolina and in a residence in Bellows Falls, Vermont.

L'Amour Directoire

Cupid, or Eros is portrayed in many concepts. In early Greek art he was depicted as a young man, later a winged youth endowed with almost feminine grace and appearance, and the Alexandrian poets pictured him as an infant, mischievous and yet at the same time malicious. He usually carried a bow and arrow or a torch and in his winged form appears with his bride Psyche, his mother Aphrodite, or Dionysus, also called Bacchus, the god of the vine and in whose name and worship the Bacchanalian orgies are held. In Hellenistic art, Erotes, cupids or putti are particularly numerous in the wall paintings of Pompeii where they are represented in all the occupations of every-day life—fishing, wine-making, weaving garlands of flowers.

Stabiae, beautifully situated on the Bay of Naples, was a favorite mineral springs resort of the ancient Romans. It was buried in the eruption of Mt. Vesuvius in A.D. 79. The cinders and ashes that entombed the city, however, preserved a colorful wall painting, now in the museum at Naples, representing a seated woman lifting an Eros out of a round cage by its wings and offering it for sale to two other women, one seated in the left foreground of the painting. In 1763 a French Artist, Vien, painted this scene and the picture gained wide notoriety in France where it was described as "artistically the revolutionary bombshell of the 18th century." Many allegorical meanings were read into the painting. The "Sale of Erotes" by Vien is now in the Palace at Fontainebleau but here in America we also had our "Sale of Loves." The engraving here illustrated was torn

THE SALE OF LOVES

Red, tan, white and green varnish
on blue-gray field

Round, 11″ diameter, 14¾″ deep

No. 20

Circa 1835

from some other publication and was then pasted into an autograph album belonging to Mary Tarbell, kept by her when she was at boarding school in Chelsea, Vermont in the 1840's. Although the poses of the figures in this engraving are slightly different in composition from the Stabiae wall painting, it nevertheless is distinctly related to that "bombshell."

The scene pictured on the wallpaper covering this bandbox might indeed serve as a sequel to the painting and engraving. Here a scantily-clad young lady in a Directoire gown has crept up on her sleeping Eros with a pair of scissors and is about to clip his wings so that never again will she have to purchase another Eros for herself.

The bandbox is a gift to the museum from Mrs. Katharine Prentis Murphy, New York and Mary Tarbell's autograph book was donated by Miss Elizabeth E. Bean, Quincy, Massachusetts.

Cietti Pompeian Panel

The papers at the bottom of this box and on the top are remnants from a panel designed by Cietti and printed by Reveillon about 1780. This pattern has been designated as a forerunner of the coarser and less delicate Pompeian styles that burst upon Paris during the Directoire period.

Cietti, an Italian, was one of the fashionable mural painters and decorators employed by Reveillon to design paper panels for use in boiserie rooms. Formerly panel paintings had been applied directly to the walls of the salons and boudoirs. They were costly decorations, and Reveillon conceived the idea of hiring the artists who were best known for this work— Huet (of textile design fame), J. S. Fay, Lavallee-Poussin, Paget and Cietti —and having them execute the same sort of decorations on paper. The panels designed by these artists as room decorations have never before or since been equalled and even in such a tiny fragment as covers the top of this box, the masterly technique of design and color can be studied.

Jean Baptiste Reveillon was a successful stationer and paper merchant and in the beginning the sale of wallpapers was only a side line with him. When he made the decision to enter the field of wallpaper manufacture, he resolved to do more than just print the flock papers so fashionable at that time. He was completely successful in his new business venture and

---

Round, 9½″ diameter, 15″ deep   No. 8   Circa 1780

Thin wood box lined with white paper and covered with two designs of block-printed wallpaper—one a white ribbon pattern on a blue field —the other white, green, blue, red, and yellow on a pale green field

eventually presented his stationery business to two of his best employees. In 1762 he leased "Folie Titon," an enormous dwelling constructed some fifty years before and surrounded by a fine park. Ten years later his business had proved so flourishing he found it necessary to construct a new building to accommodate his more than three hundred workmen. In 1784 he received from the King the title of Royal Manufactory which conveyed to him the privilege of adding the crown and three fleurs-de-lys to his trade sign. When he found he could not buy on the open market a paper fine enough to come up to his standards, he purchased a paper mill and after that his marvelous panels were issued on pure vellum paper.

Reveillon's papers were expensive luxuries, and his enemies instigated a rumor that Reveillon was going to slash the wages of his artisans in order to lower the prices on his wallpaper panels. His workmen gathered in an angry group and searched his house, but failed to find Reveillon. The mob was dispersed that first day, but the next day, April 28, 1789, they rioted again. This time they forced their way into the building, flung the furniture out-of-doors, robbed, pillaged, looted and destroyed everything they could lay their hands on. They finished off the job by setting fire to the ruins they had created. The actions of this mob have been marked by historians as the first rumblings of the French Revolution.

Embittered, Reveillon fled to England.

Griffons

This classical design wallpaper is found on four of the hat boxes or panels in the Shelburne Museum collection. All of them vary slightly in colorings and in the quality of the block impressions, which is only natural

Yellow background   50 x 12″   Panel No. 12   Circa 1830

inasmuch as the printing of the wallpaper for the band-boxes was a hand operation until about 1845.

This paper depicts a Grecian figure in chariot driving two griffons. There is a sense of action in the impelling reach of the two fabled animals and in the following drapery of the figure. The griffon (also spelled griffin or gryphon) was a mythological creature, said to be generated between the lion and the eagle. It is represented with wings, a beak and four legs, the upper part resembling an eagle, the lower portion a lion. It is seen on ancient medals and is also well known as an ornament of Greek architecture.

After Reveillon's manufactory "Folie Titon" had been pillaged and sacked by an angry pre-French Revolutionary mob, he found refuge in England. In 1781 he arranged for his wallpaper company to be operated by two men—Jacquemart and Bènard. They proved worthy successors to Reveillon, and used the same designs as well as the old techniques. Pièrre Jacquemart stayed with the company until his death in 1804 when his son succeeded him and carried on for another 36 years until he retired. In 1814, Jacquemart et Bènard issued a frieze entitled "Griffons," but whether the Griffon paper covering these bandboxes is similar to this design is not known. However, the Jacquemart et Bènard frieze may well have served as the inspiration for the design here illustrated.

Pink, white, amber varnish on blue

15 x 13, 11½″ deep   Box No. 69   16 x 12½, 11″ deep   Box No. 77

Circa 1830   Circa 1830

Pink, white and green varnish on blue background

50½ x 10″   Panel No. 4   Circa 1835

Heraea Games

Olympic Games, the principal athletic meets of ancient Greece were held in the summer once every four years at Olympia, from earliest times the center of worship of Zeus, the mightiest of Greek Gods and the site of his great temple. Traditionally they were initiated in 776 B.C. and were not discontinued until the end of the 4th century A.D. However, "women,

20 x 18, 13″ deep

Box No. 84

Also top of Box No. 64

foreigners, dishonored persons and slaves" were forbidden to compete. Not only were women prohibited from participation, but they were not even permitted to attend the games.

Consequently the women of Greece organized their own games and called them Heraea in honor of Hera, Queen of the Olympian Gods. They too were held every four years, but consisted of fewer events. Traditionally it was Hippodameia, the Grecian princess offered by her father as a prize to any man who could defeat him in a chariot race, who established the

Heraea somewhere around the 6th century. These games were discontinued about the time the Romans conquered Greece.

Feminine victors in contests were crowned with chaplets of wild olive or laurel, just as the masculine champions were honored. Male winners of the laurel wreaths were said to have esteemed them more highly than battle honors. In the beginning Olympic games included only foot races and running events, but over the years they were enlarged to include other new contests. Chariot racing was added to the competition in 680 B.C.

The games were revived in Athens in 1896, largely through the efforts of Pièrre, Baron de Coubertin, of France. Olympic events for women made their first appearance in the 1912 games and have become increasingly important.

The bandbox here illustrated depicts the winner of the team chariot race and the panel (top of page 148) portrays a chariot drawn by a single horse, the design framed in a rondelle of foliage designs, dots and dashes.

Anthemion

The paper on this box is of the Empire period (1804–14) and features the anthemion, a stylized type of Greek honeysuckle, feathered arrows crossing scrolls and other Directoire-inspired motifs; which are shown in jewel-like colors.

With the ending of the French Revolution, the period in decorative arts

Red, green, touches of white; gold varnish on pink background

22 x 17, 14″ deep

Box No. 76

Gift of Mr. Richard Gipson and Mr. Roger Wentworth, Arlington, Vermont

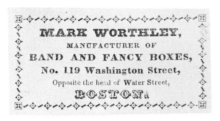

known as the "Directoire" was commenced. Although some of the flowers and scrolls of the Louis kings were retained, a neo-classic type of design became popular. The cockade of the Republic, the Phrygian cap of liberty and other symbols of the new republic were shown, but they were disciplined by geometrical designs or arrangements in diagonal bands or by being contained within medallions, lozenges or hexagons. Sheaves of wheat, festoons of laurel and roses shared space with the Greek honeysuckle, anthemion and the crossed lances or arrows—vestigial remains of the "trophies" so popular during the Louis XVI period.

Napoleon appropriated an Imperial Roman style befitting an emperor and set apart the letter "N" as his personal symbol. His laurel wreaths, bees, stars and eagles as well as Josephine's swans were added to the Greek motifs of the Directoire. Mythological gods and goddesses of war with their insignia (the thunderbolt of Jupiter, the helmet of Minerva) were also borrowed. Thus the Empire style was a composite of Greek, Roman and Egyptian art grafted to the lush remains of the Chinoiserie and the dainty floral designs made popular by Madame du Barry plus the smart simplicity of the flowers and rosebuds adored by Marie Antoinette.

The box itself was fabricated between 1839 and 1845, for the trade card pasted inside the cover gives the address of Mark Worthley, the manufacturer as 119 Washington Street in Boston. He moved from this address in 1845.

Empire Garden Scenes

A pumpkin-colored Empire paper said to represent the little King of Rome, Napoleon and Marie Louise's son, "allowed to play in the gardens at Malmaison" has been found in two houses in Massachusetts and also on the walls of a house located in Clermont, New Hampshire. This paper has been illustrated in Nancy McClelland's book *Historic Wall-papers*.

These two fragments of wallpaper that once covered a bandbox show the same dotted pumpkin-colored background and are believed to represent

Napoleon and Josephine, and Josephine about to embrace the "Eaglet" who is accompanied by his leashed dog and a little cupid or eros.

Napoleon, at the time of his divorce, cautioned the people of France that Josephine was still to receive their homage and respect. Describing her during his exile at St. Helena he mentioned that she was grace personified. "Everything she did was with a peculiar grace and delicacy. I never saw her act inelegantly during the whole time we lived together. . . . Her toilet was a perfect arsenal and she effectually defended herself against the assaults of time."

Napoleon dearly loved his little son in whose favor he abdicated in 1815. Napoleon II spent his life as a virtual prisoner in Vienna and died of

Pink, blue, white and green varnish on yellow field

13 x 33″ Panel No. 19   Circa 1815

tuberculosis when he was 21 years old. After Napoleon I was banished to St. Helena, he took with him only a few decorative accents to brighten his exile. Over his mantlepiece hung a portrait of Marie Louise, a miniature picture of the Empress Josephine, and four or five portraits of the young Napoleon, "one of which was embroidered by the hand of the mother." A small marble bust of his son stood on the mantle. The only ornaments in his spare surroundings were the "alarm chamber-watch of Frederick the Great, obtained at Potsdam, and the consular watch engraved and hung by a chain of plaited hair of Marie Louise."

More than a century was to elapse before Napoleon and his son were re-united. In 1940 Adolph Hitler as a gift to France had the little "eaglet" transferred from Vienna to the Dome of the Invalides in Paris, where his remains now rest beside his father.

See page 7 for a bandbox showing Napoleon and his son about 1820.

White and amber varnish on faded tan background

29 x 8"   Panel No. 28

Castles in Spain

Probably the early Greeks and Romans, as well as the ancient Egyptians, had their dreams of "castles in Spain" or in some equally highly improbable place where it would be impossible to acquire the land, to say nothing of affording the castle. The French used the expression "a house in Spain" to denote the same wishful dream architecture, from as early as the 14th century. Our actual expression comes from the circa 1400 translation of "The Romaunt of the Rose" in which the couplet appears:

> "Thou shalt make castles then in Spain
> And dream of joy, all but in vain."

Castles were a favorite decoration on the wallpapers covering bandboxes, as may be seen from the enormous number of examples extant in the Shelburne Museum collection. They can be seen as the cover motif most frequently, but sometimes are found on the sides of the bandbox as well. All of these examples date about 1835.

Pink and olive green varnish on yellow background. Castle and Mill design	Pink, white and olive varnish on yellow background, Castle and Mill design
15½ x 12½" Top No. 13	18 x 14" Top to box No. 7

Pink, white and dark green varnish
on blue, Castle and Mill

19 x 14"   Top No. 14

Pink, white and olive varnish on
yellow, Castle and Mill

20 x 15"   Top to box No. 33

Two other variants of the "Castle in Spain" architecture are shown. This box top belongs to the bandbox illustrated on page 100. Here the castle is seen from a distant point of land. The enclosing wreath of flowers on many of these tops substantiate the belief that separate designs were block printed and intended to be used only as cover motifs.

Pink, white and olive green varnish
on a yellow field

17 x 14"   Top of box No. 37

This cover design is found on the "Peep at the Moon" bandbox on page 195. Here the castle is situated on a rocky island. The sailboat on the lake is probably intended to act as a ferry from one castle to another. Perhaps these castles are all supposed to represent "moon architecture."

Pink, white and amber varnish on
green background

18 x 14"   Top to box No. 158

The Lute Player

The wallpaper covering these bandboxes depicts a turbaned Arab on his stead, bidding a fond farewell to his beloved who sits twanging the strings of her lute. The lute was originally an Arabian stringed instrument and is characterized by its mandolin-shaped body and neck bent to form a sharp angle. The strings are vibrated with the fingers, whereas the mandolin's metal strings in pairs are played with a plectrum, a small triangular piece of thin ivory, metal or shell.

Pink, white and amber varnish on yellow background

18 x 14, 13″ deep

No. 138   Circa 1835

The wallpaper is one of the romantic designs such as James H. Foster of Boston advertised in the *New England Palladium* as being for sale in 1817 at his shop:

> Rich paper hangings just received. Sets of the River Bosphorus. Ditto English Gardens * Captain Cook's Voyage. Views of Switzerland—Hindostan Scenery—Likewise views in Italy—Water scenes. Views in Turkey—Roman Scenery. Elysian Fields, Grecian Arcadia and many other landscape papers, making as great a variety as can be found at any store in town and at the lowest prices. . . . A great variety of French common papers and a general assortment of American Papers and Borders.

Pink and white with amber varnish on a blue field

19 x 15, 13″ deep

No. 80   Circa 1835

Turkish Inhabitants

These two hat box covers depict Turks in their national dress. Much interest centered about the inhabitants of this section of the world during the first quarter of the 19th century. Greece had been a province of Turkey and for four centuries lay under the grinding oppression of the Mahometan conquerors. In 1821 the population rose in insurrection and declared their independence from Turkey. Public opinion in the United States, and indeed all over the world, favored the Greeks.

Pink, white and green varnish on blue ground

17 x 13½″   Top No. 1

also Top of box No. 152

Circa 1830

Red, white and pale green varnish on blue ground

16 x 14″   Top No. 11

Circa 1830

Goodrich's *Pictorial Geography of the World* published 1840 gives 16 pages to European Turkey and describes the peoples as follows:

The Turks are perhaps, with regard to form and feature, the finest race of men in Europe. Their life is one of ease; their dress is loose and flowing and without the ligatures so common in the west of Europe; their ablutions are frequent, and their women have for ages been selected for beauty from the Greeks, Circassians and Georgians; with all these circumstances, it would be strange if the Turks were not a handsome race. . . . The Turks are temperate in their food, of which rice forms the principal share. . . . Wine, which was interdicted by Mahomet, is now freely drunk. . . . The pipe, however, affords the chief pleasure, or rather employment, to a Turk. The use of it is universal and almost uninterrupted. On horseback, riding, sitting, walking, reclining, or laboring at his art, it is a constant companion. It is one of the few things on which the Turks display much splendor or taste. It is always sumptuous, with those who can afford it. The tube is sometimes six or seven feet in length, and the bowl is richly ornamented. . . . No people have such indifference to shedding blood; A turk regards the life of a dog more than that of a man. This is from respect to Quithmer, the dog of the seven sleepers, whom they believe slipped into Paradise, where he now presides over letters missive, and a Mussulman writes Quithmer on the corner of his letter, after cutting a piece from it to show the imperfection of all human works.

The dress of the Turks is not liable to sudden change. . . . On the head is a turban, or a cap surrounded by many folds of cloth. The form and size are various, and denote the rank of the wearer. The Turks never uncover their heads. The Turkish dress is loose and flowing; the outward garment is a long and loose robe. Underneath is a wide vest bound with a sash; loose drawers and a shirt with wide sleeves, without wristbands. On the feet are worn slippers, which on entering a house are left at the door. This is the usual dress, though many classes have a different one.

The Promenade

The couple, out for their afternoon promenade while making the "Grand Tour" have come upon two figures in Oriental or Turkish dress sitting beside a stone monument. The couple are in costume dating about 1835 and the high-waisted, slim Directoire or Empire style in vogue just a few years before had given way to a sashed-at-the-waistline, full-skirted, full-sleeve dress.

Wallpaper manufacturers were not above "receiving inspiration" from one another's designs, and the posture and positioning of the couple here shown is so similar to the figures in the re-edited edition of *Le Petit Décor* that it is more than coincidental. The first edition of *Le Petit Décor* printed by Joseph Dufour of Paris was issued about 1815 with Directoire costumes on all his figures. In a later edition, the lady and her escort were given costumes of about 1830. This harmless deception was carried still further when the background blocks of *Le Petit Décor* were printed on a "new" paper called "The Cid" which portrayed the adventures of "the bravest knight of his age, the most virtuous and generous of men, Rodrigo Dias de Rivar, of Spain, surnamed the Cid." Through a miracle best understood by block printers of the era, the figures were metamorphosed into Spanish types, and the nursemaid who had flirted with the gay soldier in *Le Petit Décor*, now changed to a Spanish cavalier with his guitar in The Cid. This transformation was not as difficult as it might seem to the uninitiated. The papers were all hand-printed in opaque colors with carved blocks and it was a simple task to substitute blocks for the costume printing.

White, red and amber varnish on blue background

20 x 16, 12″ deep

No. 117   Circa 1835

A double design paper, mounted sideways. See page 161.
Pink, white and olive varnish on yellow background

20 x 17, 16″ deep   No. 155   Circa 1835

Oh! Leave Me to My Sorrow

Then heed not my pensive hours,
Nor bid me be cheerful now,
Can sunshine raise the flowers
That droop on a blighted bough?
The lake of the tempest wears not
The brightness its slumber wore;
The heart of the mourner cares not
For joys, that were dear before.

    Written, composed and arranged for the piano forte by Thomas Moore, Godey *Lady Book*, September 1832.

Pink and white, amber varnish on pink ground

17 x 13½″   Top No. 10

Circa 1835

"Remember Me!"

When another one's hand in the dance's wild maze,
Enrapturedly presses your own;
When your beauties, revealed to another one's gaze,
Inspire another's love tone,
           Remember me!
In those happy moments so brilliant and gay
When time on joy's light pinions flies,
Ah, then think of him, who though far, far away,
Still blesses his Julia, and sighs,
           Remember me!
       Godey *Lady Book*, August 1832.

    This was probably the original French design from which the other two treatments were copied.

Pink, white and green varnish on blue

18 x 15″   Top No. 7

Circa 1835

The box from which this panel was taken was lined with the newspaper *The Whig* published in Baltimore, June 22, 1844 and promotes: "For President—Henry Clay; for Vice President—Theodore Frelinghuysen; for Governor—Thomas G. Pratt of P. George's."

Pink, white and amber varnish on yellow background

14″ x 12   Panel No. 33   Circa 1844

Pink, white and olive-green varnish
on yellow field

15 x 12″   Top of Box No. 11

Circa 1835

Pastoral

This bandbox, one of the heaviest and sturdiest in the museum collection is covered with a French hand-blocked wallpaper, now much faded, which has been reproduced by Jones & Erwin, of New York. In the reproduced version, the shepherd and shepherdess have been placed within a framework of S-scrolls and dots enclosed in bands. Alternating with the pastoral vignettes are hexagonal figures encompassing baskets of fruit and flowers. This second design was taken from another wallpaper of the period and the two motifs were combined.

When wallpapers covering bandboxes are chosen for reproduction, the usual procedure is to carefully remove the paper from the bandboxes, repaste it in a proper repeat and then make a tracing of the design. This is necessary because in the majority of cases, the wallpapers covering the bandboxes are pasted to the boxes in a capricious manner and with no apparent effort to match up the parts of the pattern at the join.

Heavy wood box with thick wood top. Pink, red and green varnish on pale green field with white dots

17½ x 15, 10″ deep　　　　No. 78

Paper dates circa 1800

*Gift of Miss Anne Herman and
Mr. Whitfield, New York*

An Alarming Adventure

The Promenade (see page 157) is one of the designs featured on the block-printed paper covering this bandbox, and the other shows a startled girl who has been frightened by the appearance of a dog with horns or a crown of branches sprouting from his head. The young lady has sought protection in the arms of a conveniently located stalwart cavalier. In the background are foliaceous arches and a colonnaded Greek Temple. This tableau probably illustrates a popular novel of the era, but research has not yet identified the scene or persons depicted.

One half of the paper covering the box has been mounted sideways and the top is covered with a double design of identical motifs.

Pink, white and olive green varnish
on a yellow background

20 X 17, 16″ deep

No. 155   Circa 1830–40

Eros with Chaplets

Two large and out-of-scale winged cupids, poised in mid-air, hold a wreath above the head of a graceful, Empire-gowned feminine figure who reclines against a mossy hillock. She caresses a wooly white lamb. This pastoral scene is repeated three times under a tasselated design of shallow swags which mark the top of the box. A number of broad floral festoons isolate the repeats from one another. Top of this box is "Turkish Inhabitants" scene, on page 155.

Pink, white and green varnish on
yellow background

18 X 12, 11″ deep

No. 152   Circa 1830–40

Pink, white and amber varnish on blue

48½ x 12″   Panel No. 5   Circa 1835

Basket of Fruits

Still-life baskets of fruits, such as the one depicted on this bandbox panel appear in many guises in the Shelburne Museum collection. They were favorite subject matter of the young ladies who attended the "Female Seminaries." Course of Study in a seminary such as the one established in Burlington, Vermont in 1835 occupied three years unless the Young Lady pursued the Latin Language, in which case four years was required. An equivalent portion of the time, if she did not take Latin, was devoted to either music, French or drawing. The tuition per quarter in the English Branches and Latin was five dollars; drawing and painting in water colors was four dollars extra and oil painting was listed at six dollars extra per quarter. Board, including fuel, lights and washing came to twenty-five dollars per quarter.

Professor J. H. Hills taught "drawing and crayoning" to the young ladies and painting on velvet in oils was surely one of the artistic expressions the teen-agers learned from their preceptor. To compose their paintings they chose a variety of stencils or theorems, as they were called, of various fruits and then disposed them artistically, according to their individual taste. The finished painting on velvet was similar to the basket of fruits on this panel.

The height of the little figures is completely out of proportion in comparison with the fruit basket, but this adds to the primitive appeal of this hand-blocked wallpaper design.

Children's Games

THE SWING

How do you like to go up in a swing,
  Up in the air so blue
Oh! I do think it the pleasantest thing
  Ever a child can do.

This fragment of a bandbox is lined with Philadelphia newspapers dating in 1839.

Pink, white and green varnish on green background

16 x 13″

Panel No. 32

DANCING DOGS

A young lad with flute pipes a playful tune and the four dogs, decked in Directoire style human finery dance a merry ballet. The boy's right hand raps out a gay rat-a-tat beat on a drum.

Red, white and green varnish on blue background, dots in deeper blue fill in background

15 x 19″

Top to box No. 137

Circa 1835

A GAME OF MARBLES AND
FEEDING THE CHICKENS

This bandbox features two different designs, each appearing twice.

Marbles in one form or another have been played in America since Colonial times and even before that American Indians played a game similar to one Colonists had played in England. Ancient Chinese played with them as early as 4,000 B.C. and Romans amused themselves with the little glass balls before the Punic Wars. Here our three young lads are entertaining themselves with this age-old sport.

The other design shows a little girl teasing her dog with a dangling handkerchief. Her playmate holds the dog by his collar while the chicken waits patiently for the grain the little girl is supposed to be feeding to her.

Red, white and green varnish on blue background

16 x 12¾, 11½″ deep   No. 133   Circa 1835

HISTORICAL DESIGNS
COMMEMORATING
PEOPLE AND PLACES

Castle Garden

The building illustrated on this bandbox has served many purposes in its 150 years. Commenced in 1808 as a defense for the New York Harbor in the war of 1815 it was first known as West Battery and then as Castle Clinton. Although garrisoned during this war, it became better known as the first port of entry when Lafayette returned to the United States for his 1824 visit. For this occasion it was lavishly decorated and served as a backdrop for a harbor full of welcoming boats bedecked with gala flags.

That same year the fort was leased to private individuals by the City of New York to whom it had been ceded by the Federal Government. It then served as a concert hall for about 30 years. The hat box shown here depicts the building during this period. Source for the block-printed view is a lithograph issued by Alexander J. Davis, published by Imbert & Company, just prior to 1830.

One of the most famous concerts of all time was the recital of Jenny Lind, the "Swedish Nightingale" who made her American debut at Castle Garden in September of 1850. A crowd of 5,000 persons was present at

Pink, white and olive green varnish on yellow field

18 x 14, 11" deep No. 7

Circa 1830-40

this first concert. P. T. Barnum in his *Recollections* described his arrangements of the room for this concert:

> The great parterre and gallery of Castle Garden were divided by imaginary lines into four compartments, each of which was designated by a lamp of a different color. The tickets were printed in colors corresponding with the location which the holders were to occupy, and one hundred ushers, with rosettes and bearing wands tipped with ribbons of the several hues, enabled every individual to find his or her seat without the slightest difficulty. Every seat was of course numbered in color to correspond with the check, which each person retained after giving up an entrance ticket at the door. Thus tickets, checks, lamps, rosettes, wands and even the seat numbers were all in the appropriate colors to designate the different departments. These arrangements were duly advertised. . . . The consequence was, that although about 5,000 persons were present at the first concert, their entrance was marked with as much order and quiet as was ever witnessed in the assembling of a congregation at church.

Three years later, Castle Garden became the reception center for the steady stream of immigrants, largely from England, Ireland and Germany who poured into this country. During the period 1880–84 almost 2,000,000 alien immigrants arrived at New York. Though many of them stayed in the metropolitan area (of the city's 1,209,561 people in 1880, the census counted only 727,000 as native), thousands went west. Cash value of railroad tickets sold to immigrants at the Castle Garden Depot in 1881 was more than $5,000,000. In 1892 the U.S. Immigration Station removed to Ellis Island, but the old building did not remain unused for long. Turned back to the city of New York, it was known and enjoyed by several more

Pink, yellow and green varnish with white touches on blue background. This is a double printed paper (other design is Rustic Bridge, illustrated on page 45).

17 x 20, 14″ deep   No. 91

generations as the Aquarium—the city's chief show place with its millions of visitors every year.

In 1946 it was decided to tear the venerable structure down, but through the efforts of civic and patriotic bodies, headed by the New-York Historical Society, the old fort was saved. It reverted to the Federal Government and will be restored by the National Park Service to its original condition as a national monument of distinction.

The respected edifice has also served as a decorative motif in many ways. Lafayette's visit was duly recorded in an engraving which served as source for a Staffordshire china pattern issued by James and Ralph Clews. The same view of Castle Garden illustrated on this hat box was reproduced in three variants by other Staffordshire potters. Enoch Wood called his design "Castle Garden"; Ralph Stevenson named his "Esplanade and Castle Garden, New York" and J. & J. Jackson issued his adaptation under the title of "New York, Battery etc."

Sandy Hook

Nineteen miles seaward from New York on the western side of the Bay, is a narrow strip of white sand projecting northward into the bright waters . . . On a clear day it gleams like a streak of polished silver, but when the skies are dull and gray or overhung with clouds, it lies leaden and dead in the half light. This is Sandy Hook, a long, low sandy peninsula of drift formation—the continuation of a sand reef skirting the New Jersey coast . . . This spot has been the site of one of the principal lighthouses on our coast from a very early period of our history.

New York by Sunlight and Gaslight, James D. McCabe, 1881.

The merchants of New York realized the need to establish a light on this dangerous reef and in 1761 took steps to raise the money by having

Rose, white and green on a blue background

50 x 11″ Panel No. 1   About 1830–35

two lotteries authorized by the New York Assembly. The lighthouse was completed and the lamps lit three years later. The structure was of stone and measured from the surface of the ground to the top of the lighthouse 106 feet. During the American Revolution, the Provincial Congress caused the lights to be removed, but during a later period of the war the building was fortified and occupied by the British.

The exterior of the lighthouse was retained in its original form but interior improvements made before 1881 included lining the interior with brick and replacing the wooden stairs with iron steps. The lens was of French construction and was 90 feet from the ground. The lighthouse keeper had his little cottage at the foot of the tower with pleasant shade trees and a pretty garden. His barn and cow sheds were built of drift wood that had been cast ashore by the merciless waves.

During the last years of the 18th century, John Davis, British author and tutor travelled in the United States and he reported that on March 18th 1798 he had visited Sandy Hook, but found there only one "human habitation which was a public house. The family consisted of an old woman, wife to the landlord, two young girls of homely appearance, a negro man and boy. While breakfast was preparing I ascended with my companions the light house, which stood on the point of the Hook. It was lofty and well furnished with lamps."

Two ships under full sail are shown racing toward the light in the bandbox panel with the legend "Sandy Hook." The same view appears on one of the box tops in the museum collection also.

Pink, white and dark green varnish on blue background

17 X 13″   Top No. 6   About 1830–35

New York Institution for the Blind

This blue paper-covered trade box shows an engraved tradecard imprinted with a building and with the legend "Manufactured at The New-York Institution for the Blind, Ninth Avenue, from 33rd to 34th Street." It belonged to Abraham Storm and his name and address—Dobbs Ferry—is penned on the cover.

In 1841 a book entitled *Historical Collections of the State of New York containing a General Collection of the Most Interesting Facts, Traditions, Biographical Sketches, Anecdotes, etc. relating to its History and Antiquities* was written by John Barber and Henry Howe. They reported that "at the New York Institution for the Blind there are about 50 blind pupils, who, in addition to the school exercises are employed in making baskets, mats, rugs, carpeting, and in braiding palm-leaf hats. They are also taught instrumental and vocal music."

This top was apparently part of a trade box in which were retailed the "palm leaf hats" made by the blind.

Gift of John's Antiques, New York

14 x 12″,   Top No. 24   Circa 1842

New York City Hall

Three of the bandboxes in the museum collection have tops or covers which show two different views of New York's municipal Government headquarters. This building was the third edifice to be known as the New York City Hall. The first structure was built on Pearl Street in 1642, but was sold as unsafe 57 years later. The second, finished in 1704, was destroyed in 1812. The third City Hall, designed by the architect John McComb is located in City Hall Park and is the one shown on the wall papers covering these box tops.

G. M. Davison's *Traveller's Guide*, published in 1833, mentioned that the front of the building was of white marble.

It is 216 feet long, 105 feet broad, and including the attic story, 65 feet high. The rooms for holding the different courts of law are fitted up in a rich and expensive style. The room for holding the mayor's court contains portraits of Washington, of the different governors of the state and many of the most celebrated commanders of the army and navy of the United States. The foundation stone of this building was laid in 1803, and the whole finished in 1812, at an expense of $500,000. It is one of the most elegant edifices in America and reflects great credit on the inhabitants for their munificence and taste.

Later a clock with four faces surmounting the cupola was added and in 1880 illuminated at night by gas.

The cupola was destroyed by fire and the figure of Justice fell to the ground, but traditionally the original figure was restored, given a coat of zinc or copper and used again.

An 1819 print shows Broadway and City Hall with a simple iron fence

Pink, white and green varnish on blue background

Oval 16 x 20″   Top to box No. 99   Circa 1830

and a cross surmounting the cupola, but the 1830 water color by J. W. Hill showing City Hall and Park Row included heavy stone gate posts and a much more elaborate iron fence.

In the two views found on the covers of Shelburne Museum's hat boxes, the one on page 170 probably shows the later view of City Hall as the clock visible in the cupola was installed during the years 1830–31. The shaped box cover and the faded oval cover show a foreshortened cupola without clock, but with an elaborate iron fence. The fence and gates (erected in 1817–21) were removed in 1847.

Pink, white and reddish brown varnish on yellow background

16 x 13″   Shaped cover to box No. 86   Circa 1830

Red, white and green varnish on blue background

16 x 12¾″   Cover to box No. 133   Circa 1830

Deaf and Dumb Asylum, New York City

There were deaf and dumb asylums in several cities. Philadelphia established such an asylum about 1819. The first such organization was opened at Cobbs, Virginia in 1812 and the most famous of all the deaf and dumb sanctuaries was the one founded in Hartford, Connecticut by the Rev. Thomas Hopkins Gallaudet, well known educator of the deaf, graduate of Andover Theological Seminary. In England and France he studied methods of educating the deaf and founded the first such free school in America.

We are indebted to Mr. R. W. G. Vail, Director of the New-York Historical Society for the identification and description of the building shown on this block printed panel:

> The Deaf and Dumb Asylum is positively the one in New York City. It apparently was re-drawn for the bandbox design from Theodore S. Day's *Views of New York and its Environs* published in parts in 1831. This view shows the building as it is in your picture. It was later much enlarged and improved. The Eno Collection in The New York Public Library also has the same wallpaper design in colors.
>
> The property on East 49th Street was deeded to the Institution of the City of New York in 1827. The building was located between Fifth Avenue and Fourth Avenue (now Park Avenue), Madison Avenue not having been laid out through the area at that time. The building was dedicated in September of 1829 and faced 49th Street with the rear close to the south side of 50th Street. Later on it was enlarged and the ends were considerably changed and a tower added in the middle . . . The Institution moved to its new building at Fort Washington Avenue and 164th Street in 1856 and sold the 50th Street property to Columbia University in that year. The College occupied the site and erected additional buildings until its removal to Morningside Heights in 1897. The following year the property was sold for residential purposes by the College.

Pink, white and amber
varnish on
yellow background

17 x 13″   Panel No. 42

Circa 1831

Merchant's Exchange, New York

The first Merchants Exchange was built 1825–7 on the south side of Wall Street covering the block between Wall Street, Exchange Place, William Street and Hanover Street. It was destroyed in the great fire of December 1835. The new building on the same site was designed by Isaiah Rogers, opened November 1841 and completed the following year. Leased to the United States Government for use as a Custom House in 1862, it was sold to the Government three years later. They held it until 1890 when it was purchased by National City Bank and remodeled by them from plans by McKim, Mead and White who piled another colonnaded structure atop the original building. Four stories were added in 1908 and it is still occupied by the First National City Bank today.

Our bandbox panel represents the second building before its remodeling and is described as having a Wall Street front of 144 feet, with 171 feet fronting Exchange Place. From the top of the central dome to the ground, the distance is 124 feet.

The Wall Street front is ornamented with a handsome portico supported by 12 front, four middle and two rear columns of granite, each 38 feet in height. The building is constructed of Quincy granite and its cost, including the ground in 1835 was $1,800,000. The United States Government purchased it for one million dollars and converted it to its own use . . . The Wall Street entrance leads directly to the rotunda, the main hall of the building, lying immediately beneath the dome. Around the sides of this beautiful hall are eight lofty columns of Italian marble, the superb Corinthian columns of which were carved in Italy. They support the base of the dome and are probably the largest and noblest marble columns in the United States.
New York by Sunlight and Gaslight, JAMES D. McCABE, 1881.

Gift of Mrs. Frederick B. Wright, Pelham Manor, New York

Red, white and green varnish on pale green background

36½ x 11½″ Panel No. 44   Circa 1842

Holt's New Hotel, New York City

Traveller's Guide published in 1833 described this hotel at some length. It had been opened that year by Stephen Holt and its "public ordinary was resorted to by many of the most respectable and influential men."

Holt's Hotel, forming an allinement on three streets, the one part in Water, another in Pearl and its eastern limit facing on Fulton Street, and occupying the entire block, is one of the most extensive and expensive establishments of the kind in the United States. It is built of white marble, and is six stories high, exclusive of the basement, having an attic of ample dimensions, and surmounted by a lofty quadrangular tower, around which there is an extensive and pleasant promenade. Above this is a spacious rotundo, from whose exalted summit a view is obtained of nearly the whole city, the East River, Brooklyn, part of Long Island, the entire upper bay and harbor, Staten Island, a very considerable extent of the Hudson River and the Jersey shore. In the basement story, a steam engine of 12 horse power is placed, by means of which machinery is put in motion which carries up through a perpendicular casement the cooked provision for the guests, which, by this means, is conveyed almost to the side of the table where it is to be consumed. The second floor is occupied by drawing and sitting rooms, the large dining room being 100 feet in length and 28 in breadth, well supplied with light from numerous windows and elegantly furnished. The third floor, containing parlor, dining, retiring and receiving

Pink, white and green varnish on yellow background

17 x 13, 11" deep   No. 95   Circa 1833

rooms, is exclusively appropriated to the accommodation of gentlemen having ladies and families. The other three stories and the attic are judiciously divided into sitting and lodging rooms, with parlors, all of which are furnished in a style of richness and neatness, calculated to afford comfort and a home to every inmate. On the side and in the centre of the main stairway, the dumb-waiters rise, by the aid of the steam engine in the basement, to the tower, and by the active power of this engine, and the use of forcing pumps, each story is at all times furnished with cold and hot water for the baths in the attic, and for ordinary uses in the several rooms. The house from the base to the foot of the tower is 100 feet high, and 140 to the summit. There are 165 rooms, 25 of which are parlors, 125 being lodging rooms, and the residue appropriated to other useful purposes.

This hotel changed its name to United States Hotel in 1839 and eight years later all of this magnificence was razed.

The detail shown here is an action-packed panorama and predates the candid camera technique of today. In this very busy location, a porter is seen wheeling baggage to a horse-drawn dray and the inset shows more clearly that at the end of the street there is a sailing ship and a steamboat plying the river.

Joys of Rural Life

Many of America's most distinguished men have also been avid sports-men. George Washington was an enthusiastic fox hunter and like most Tidewater gentlemen, he bred and raised race horses. Naturally he often attended the races at Annapolis to see his animals perform and history records that on one trip he dropped fifteen pounds at the track which he failed to recoup at cards that night. Washington's kennels and stables fell off badly during the Revolution, but he rebuilt them after the war. During the period of his Mount Vernon residence for the six years preceding 1789, he hunted only 23 times and killed fewer than 10 foxes. This was quite a contrast to his more active years prior to the War. His journals show that in a single year, 1768, he took the field 48 times and killed 18 foxes, once hunting five days at a stretch.

Washington's passion was horses, but he found time to fish the Potomac with both line and net for sturgeon, sheepshead and shad, and he often went gunning for wildfowl.

This sporting pattern was followed by many gentlemen of leisure, but it was a life also shared by farmers and plantation planters. It is only natural that the joys of a rural life should be depicted on the papers covering bandboxes and illustrated here are farmers fishing and riding.

Rose, white and amber varnish on yellow field

46½ x 10½"   Panel No. 13   Circa 1835

Blue, white, black and brown varnish on yellow field

49½ x 11"   Panel No. 14   Circa 1835

Pink, white and green
varnish on blue back-
ground

17 x 15″ Top to box

No. 28

Circa 1835

Two fragments pasted to cover below show a variant of the fisherman scene. There appears to be a waterfall cascading over a hillside and making the small pond where the angler is trying his luck. The tradecard pasted to the top of the box tells the variety of stock carried by L. Campbell of Plainfield, Massachusetts. "Dealer in Millinery & Fancy goods, bonnets, ribbons, feathers, artificial flowers, cheniels, collars, gloves, mits, dress caps, head dresses, laces, edgings, embroideries, trimmings, velvet ribbons, bonnet silks, velvets, lace mantillas, fancy shawls, shaker hoods, boys hats etc. Old bonnets repaired and put in fashionable shape—Mourning articles and Grave clothes made to order. Also on hand, a general assortment of dry goods, groceries, hard Ware, crockery, etc." Today Plainfield has a population of 228 persons but a century ago it was probably a much larger town and let us hope that "L. Campbell" found ready buyers for the lace mantillas and bonnet silks.

Pink, white and olive
green varnish on blue
background

16 x 12″ Top No. 18

About 1835

These two fragments of wallpaper taken from bandboxes seem to bear no relation to each other, but they depict the same farmhouse and round front yard enclosure delineated by a picket fence. A figure is visible above the lower section of the Dutch Door in both fragments.

Pink and white with dark varnish on blue background

19½ x 12½″   Panel No. 35   Circa 1835

White and red on blue background

10 x 8½″   Panel No. 34   Circa 1835

Rural Life

I think agriculture the most honorable of all employments, being the most independent. The farmer has no need of popular favor, nor of the favor of the great; the success of his crops depending only on the blessing of God and upon his honest industry.—BENJAMIN FRANKLIN.

The *Farmers' Almanac* for 1841 gave a vivid description of a poor farmer in its moral lesson for June.

A slovenly farmer may be known by his inattention to small things as well as great. The shoes of his children are spoiled for the want of strings to tie them, or a little tallow to grease them. His gate hinge comes off for the want of a nail, and the gate is destroyed for the want of a hinge, and his garden is destroyed for the want of a gate; and all this loss is occasioned by not timely driving and clinching a single nail. Nothing is in order. He has a place for nothing and nothing is in its place. If he wants a gimlet, a chissel, or a hammer, he hunts up chamber, runs out to the barn, then to the corn house, searches the cupboards, and lastly when he has spent more time in the search than it would have taken to do the job he finds it down cellar. He keeps no stock of small things—if a button or a bail to a pail gives way, or a key to a yoke or a pin to a sled, or a helve to an axe, or even a tooth to a rake, he has none to replace them. These are a few of the signs of a poor farmer. See, then, dear friend, that they are not applicable to yourself!

It is evident that the home places of the farmers depicted on these bandboxes here illustrated do not classify as the products of a "slovenly farmer."

Red and white on bright blue field

16 x 12½, 11″ deep   No. 67

Circa 1835

Rose, white and brown varnish on yellow field

43 x 10½″   Panel No. 10   Circa 1835

Pink, white and pale varnish on blue background

50 x 13½"   Panel No. 3

Unidentified Chapel and Buildings

When these bandboxes were acquired by the museum, one of them was identified as the New York State Capitol Buildings or first capitol at Albany and the others were identified as Buildings at Yale University. It was also suggested that one of the panels represented the buildings at Harvard University.

Correspondence with authorities has disclaimed all these identifications. The Curator of History of the Division of Archives and History of the University of the State of New York has pointed out: "The building used by the State Legislature when Albany first became the State Capital is obviously not the one in your photos. The first building erected by the state as a capitol was authorized in 1797 . . . It was built of brick, four stories high. In 1836 it was used for Geological Hall, forerunner of the present State Museum. It definitely is not your building. Philip Hooker designed a state capitol which was used from 1808 until the present building was erected. Again, this is not shown in your photos."

Yale University has replied: "At first glance we thought that the photographs were the Old Brick Row at Yale, but on consulting with several authorities on old buildings at Yale, we have been told that they were not Yale buildings. The designs were probably used simply for decorative purposes."

The Senior Assistant in the Harvard University Archives of the Harvard College Library stated: "We do not recognize the scenes shown in the photographs; they are not Harvard scenes."

Goodrich's *Pictorial Geography* published in Boston in 1840 shows engravings of Dartmouth, Amherst, Columbia and the University of Virginia, but the buildings shown on the hat box papers do not match up with any of these engravings. In the light of this evidence, we must agree that as Yale University has pointed out—the designs were probably used simply for decorative purposes.

The "Unidentified Chapel and Building" bandboxes in the museum collection vary in color, but they are all in the larger sizes. Because they

Pink, white and green varnish on
blue background

19 x 15, 12″ deep   No. 137

Pink, white and amber varnish on
yellow field

13 x 11½, 11½″ deep   No. 4

are all lined with white paper, there is no clue as to date to be found from newspapers. However, one of the boxes had a trade card glued to its cover showing that it came from Beebe & Costar of 196 Broadway, New York. City directories list this firm in their 1845–46 issue under the heading of "hatter." We may safely assume that the other boxes date from the same period.

Red, white and amber
varnish on blue back-
ground

11½ x 9, 11½″ deep

No. 126

The Volunteer Fireman

Shown on this bandbox is the engine received in 1830 by Eagle Engine Company #13 of New York City. Painted black with gold striping and silver-plated brass-work, it was one of the mobile, manpowered tub engines in which the stream of water came from the goose-neck pipe on top of the air chamber. Fire extinguishers of this type were patented by Richard Newsham of England about 1721–25 and the style continued both here and abroad until well into the early part of the 19th century.

Pink, white and dark varnish on blue background. Double design with Coach Scene, shown on page 117.

17 x 21, 14" deep   No. 132

About 1835

Gift of Mrs. J. C. Rathborne, Westbury, Long Island

Pasted inside the cover of this bandbox is the tradecard of Joseph S. Tillinghast of New Bedford, Massachusetts. A search of the New Bedford directories beginning in 1836 show Tillinghast in the insurance business at 99 Union Street that year. He moved about and in 1839 he is listed at 105 Union. In 1841 he moved to 58 North Water Street and was still at that address and engaged in 1849 in the insurance business. A search through newspaper advertisements do not show him in the paper business in 1822 or 1829 so it is believed that he must have sold imported and American paper hangings not before 1830 and not later than 1835.

Compare the bandbox opposite with the one illustrated above. Here the design has been copied, but in duplicating the design, the wood block carver copied the design instead of reversing it. Consequently, when printed, the entire scene is transposed which shows up in the reversed number (13) on the engine. This box is lined with *Miners' Journal of Pottsville, Pa.* and

Pink and white, reddish varnish on
yellow background

16 x 13, 14¾" deep   No. 86

About 1830

mentions dates in July, May and June of 1829. Top is lined with *York
Republican and Anti-Masonic Exposition* and the bottom is re-inforced with
a German-language newspaper.

The ubiquitous British sight-seer, Capt. Marryat, in his *Diary in
America* published in the 1830's poked fun at our volunteer fireman system.
He lodged opposite two fire engine houses while in New York and noted
that he could always tell when a fire broke out, but then he added:

> Everybody always knows when there is a fire, for the church nearest to the
> fire tolls its bell and this tolling is repeated by all the others; and as there are
> more than 300 churches in New York, if a fire takes place, no one can say
> that he is not aware of it.
>
> The duty of firemen is admirably performed by the young men of the city
> who have privileges for a servitude of 7 years; but they pay too dearly for
> their privileges, which are an exemption from militia and jury summons.
> Many of them are taken off by consumptions, fevers, and severe catarrhs,

engendered by the severe trials to which they are exposed; the sudden transitions from extreme heat to extreme cold in winter, being summoned up from a warm bed when the thermometer is below zero—then exposed to the scorching flames—and afterwards (as I have frequently seen them myself) with the water hanging in icicles upon their saturated clothes. To recruit themselves after their fatigue and exhaustion, they are compelled to drink, and thus it is no wonder that their constitutions are undermined. It is nevertheless a favourite service, as the young men have an opportunity of shewing courage and determination, which raises them high in the opinion of their brother citizens.

Les Trois Jours, *The Three Days*

This bandbox commemorates the revolutionizing three days—July 27, 28 and 29, 1830 and the battle to restore Louis Philippe to the throne of France. Godey's *Lady Book* summarized Louis Philippe's life when in a brief sketch of the reigning monarch of France it stated; "Seldom indeed has fortune exercised her dispensations more capriciously than in directing the existence of the present king of the French through its various phases. A prince, a conqueror, a refugee, a martyr, an exile—a lieutenant general today; a king tomorrow . . . Once the most remote aspirant to the throne of his ancestors . . . now enjoying and dispensing the fortunes of a monarchy."

Born at Paris in 1773, Louis was educated in France and at 18 placed himself at the head of the 14th regiment of dragoons. Although he dis-

Gift of Mrs. Katharine Prentis Murphy, New York

Red, white, green and yellow on a pale blue-green field

16 x 11, 11″ deep   No. 25   Circa 1830

tinguished himself in battle, he was forced to quit both the army and his country because of "too openly manifesting his hostility to the revolutionary excesses in France." Wandering through Switzerland as a fugitive, he taught under an assumed name in the college at Richenan for awhile. He was able to get a Swiss passport as a tourist and journeyed through the Scandinavian countries until he sailed for America, arriving in Philadelphia in 1796. For the next two years he visited Virginia, Maryland and the New England states. He set sail aboard an American vessel in 1798, but this ship was captured by an English frigate and the unhappy Duke of Chartres (as he was called at that time) was summarily put ashore at Havana. Forced to leave Cuba, the Duke and his brothers found refuge with the Duke of Kent in the English Bahamas and it was through his efforts that Louis was finally allowed to debark in London in 1800. Nine years later his marriage to the daughter of the King of Sicily took place. Upon the fall of Napoleon, he repaired to Paris, but was again forced to flee to England in 1815. When Louis XVII was restored to the throne in France, the Duke was allowed to return to his homeland. In the year 1824 he was given the title of Royal Highness. After the battle smoke of the momentous "Three days" had settled, Louis was invited to assume executive power as Lieutenant General of the Kingdom. Upon the abdication of Charles X and his son, Louis assumed the title of King of the French and took the name of Louis Philip(pe) I.

Louis became known as "the Citizen King" and his queen with their five sons and three daughters made up what was referred to as "the foremost Bourgeois family in France."

In the block-printed battle scene on this bandbox, the banner carried by the young street fighter bears the dates "27, 28 & 29 Juillet 1830" and on the cover the chanticleer with the two draped flags proclaims the new look in French government—"Ordre Liberté."

Port de Calais, Chateau de Blaye, France

Two views are featured in the engraving, tinted with water colors, pasted to the sides of this box. One is the "Vue du Port de Calais," which Goodrich's *1840 Pictorial Geography* noted was "remarkable as the nearest point of approach between England and France, being but two and a half hours from Dover." On the opposite side of the box is the "Vue du Chateau de Blaye." Blay is located in France off the Bay of Biscay and not far from Bordeaux. Titles identifying these engravings are turned over and pasted inside the top rim of the box. Lettering is reversed on both the titles. The cover of the box presents another engraving—the head and shoulders of a most attractive young lady (see page 69). This fashion print has also been tinted. Inside the cover is pasted a fine quality writing paper with columns of figures under the heading, "Trial Balance for August 1836."

Round, 10″ diam. 10″ deep   No. 98

Circa 1836

George Washington

Lines written on the Character of Washington

Washington he was an hero bold, likewise a man of fame
And Children yet unborn shall rise to bless and praise his name
Through trials and through suffrings his pathway it did lead
He proved himself to be a friend just in the time of need.

The joys of home he did resign, likewise the fireside
And for to face the enemy he traveled far and wide
View him in Canada, tho young, a man of courage bold
When shot like hail around him flew, his courage did not cold.

But he obeyed his country's call a general for to be
He led his troops like heros on to gain sweet liberty
A Caezer fought, he gained the world, such thing I have been told
But when compared with Washington he was not half so bold.

Wellington he fought but never gained such blessings for his nation
For in the face of thousands I have seen marked starvation
Napoleon fought, he fought quite brave to gratify his pride
His day of victory never came, he bowed his head and died.

Nothing but liberty, on it Washington was bent
And tho at last he did become a faithful President
And now from Monarch's pride we feel a sweet release
And with all neighboring nations we are happily at peace.

If a foreign foe invade this land, we'll turn out to a man
We are sure to fight them boldly, we'll do the best we can
Though Washington is dead and he is gone to rest
We know the very same spirit dwells in the Yankee's breast.

And now to Washington a monument we'll raise
That ages yet unborn may learn to speak of him with praise.

This unpublished poem was found in the notebook kept by William Wallis who wrote the eulogy in 1844. Wallis, an immigrant from Froome, Somersetshire, England came to America and after residing within its borders for five years took out his citizenship papers in 1846 at Windsor County, Vermont. Wallis is buried at the cemetery in Cavendish, Vermont.

The wallpaper covering this bandbox shows a centered cartouche with the bust of the hero in his uniform as general of the armies. Above and below the portrait are other framed vignettes and almost illegible titles de-

Blue, tan and white with touches of
red on a beige tan field

12 x 9¼, 9″ deep   No. 93

Circa 1815

scribe the scenes depicted: "Entrance into New York"; "Battle of Monmouth"; "Surrender of Cornwallis" and on the cover—"Crossing of the Delaware."

William Henry Harrison

This bandbox commemorates an exciting political period in the history of our country. Harrison was the candidate put forward by the Whig Party for the presidential election in 1840. His attributes included a good military record and reputation as a daring Indian fighter plus a happy home life with his wife who had borne him 10 children. The democratic incumbent was Martin Van Buren, the widower president who had restored to the White House the civility befitting the dignity of the Chief Executive's residence and an atmosphere of elegance.

The Whigs waged their campaign on personality differences of the candidates after a Democratic newspaper commented editorially that "Upon condition of his receiving a pension of $2,000 and a barrel of cider, General Harrison would no doubt consent to withdraw his presidential pretensions and spend his days in a log cabin on the banks of the Ohio." The bandbox here illustrated depicts the general in just this setting—even to the barrel of cider leaning against the cabin wall and the sidewheeler in the river with

Ohio painted on as a paddlewheel decoration. A wounded veteran being made welcome by the general (in shirtsleeves) adds an appealing touch.

Enemies of Van Buren seized every opportunity to accuse him of wanton extravagance—he was reviled for his elegance and his effeminacy (Van, Van, is a used-up man). The representative from Pennsylvania denounced him in the famous Gold Spoon Speech for his extravagance and aristocracy: "Your house glitters with all imaginable luxuries and gaudy ornaments. . . . How delightful it must be to be a real genuine Loco Foco. . . . To sip with a golden spoon his soup à la Reine from a silver tureen." These much-maligned spoons were not gold, but gold-plated; they were not new; they did not belong to Van Buren, but had been a part of the White House table service for almost 20 years—but no matter—it was a good jibe. Taunts such as this had much to do with the defeat of Van Buren. The Whigs had no platform; they avoided the issues and staged a theatrical campaign that bordered on hysteria. Effigies, huge political rallies, crazy hats, floats, campaign songs *Tippecanoe and Tyler Too*—each week brought new surprises. The "plain country boy" (who at 68 was the oldest president to be inaugurated and incidentally the first to die in office) was swept to victory. His triumph, however, was short-lived. Exactly one month after he had taken office he was dead of "bilious pleurisy"—probably what we know as pneumonia today. The news was delivered to his wife in North Bend, Ohio just as she was about to leave their home to join him in Washington.

Pink, white and olive green varnish on blue field

14 x 11½, 10" deep   No. 71   Circa 1840

Andrew Jackson, Old Hickory

Although in poor condition, this hat box is of historical interest to the museum collection. It depicts "Old Hickory" in his younger days and the view has been suggested by the engraving after T. Sully which shows Jackson with his sword and horse.

Andrew Jackson was the first American president who was not of either the Virginia or Massachusetts aristocracy. His life was a hard one and from the day he was born, he seemed to be dogged by sorrow and grief. His father, a tenant farmer of North Ireland migrated to this country in 1765, but lived only two years after settling his family in the wilderness of North Carolina. Destitute, his widow took refuge with a sister in South Carolina where Andrew was born in a log cabin just a few weeks after his father's death.

At the age of 14, Andrew was left alone in the world, having lost both his brothers and his mother within a single year. It is no wonder that he grew up wild and earned a reputation as a tavern brawler and gambler—the "head of the rowdies hereabouts." During this period of his life, however, he studied law and at 20 was admitted to the bar. During the 1790's he became the most successful lawyer in Nashville and served as Tennesee's first representative in Congress after that state was admitted to the union. Now wealthy, he wanted to retire and live the relaxed life of a gentleman farmer and with this in mind he established Hermitage plantation in 1804—the grandest and finest home in the State.

His dream of a quiet life was soon shattered, for once again his state called upon him for help. This time he was given command of the Tennesee troops and in one great battle at Horseshoe Bend on the banks of the Tallapoosa River (in present Alabama) Jackson broke the Creek warriors on March 27 of 1814 and forced their leader William Weatherford, whose Indian name was Red Eagle, to make peace with the Great White Father in Washington.

Fifteen years later, the military hero, Old Hickory, became president of the United States, but it was with a heavy heart that he assumed office. His beloved wife, Rachel, had died just six weeks after the election, killed, her husband believed by malicious slander. He was forevermore embittered against his political opponents who had raked up the incident of Rachel's first marriage and subsequent re-marriage to Jackson before her divorce had been finalized.

Jackson was a moody and controversial figure during the years he served as president, from 1829 to 1837. He is still remembered as a president who rode rough-shod over the laws where they conflicted with his personal opinions and who summarily dismissed any cabinet minister who ventured to oppose or disagree with him. However prejudiced and vindictive he may have been toward his enemies, he was nevertheless warm, generous and absolutely loyal to his friends.

An examination of the bandbox here shown will expose that the green varnish used in the grass and on the trees covers up the legend originally printed on this box. A rendering of a similar bandbox filed with the Index of American Design establishes that the figure shown on our box was meant to portray Andrew Jackson. On a ribbon caught in the branches of the tree is the evidence; the warrior hero is "Old Hickory" as he was known by his admirers.

Thin wood box. Red, white and green varnish on yellow field

19 x 15½, 11″ deep   No. 58   About 1840

National Gallery of Art, American Index of Design rendering by Harold Merriam, Bandbox owned by New Haven Colony Historical Society, Conn.

Blue, brown and white on grey background

15 x 12½, 10″ deep   No. 168   Circa 1846

Gen. Zachary Taylor, Old Rough and Ready

Texas was annexed to the United States in 1845 and along with the new state, the U.S. inherited the Texans' conflict with Mexico. Upon declaring their independence from Mexico, Texas had claimed as its boundary the Rio Grande River. When Mexico refused to receive an American representative after the annexation, President Polk ordered Gen. Zachary Taylor to move into the disputed territory and establish himself on the banks of the Rio Grande.

With nearly 4,000 troops and a few mounted volunteers, Taylor proceeded to build a fort opposite the Mexican town of Metamoros. After completion of the Fort, Taylor withdrew the bulk of his army to the main base at Point Isabel, leaving a small detachment of artillery with instructions to fire the heavy siege guns at regular intervals should the Fort be attacked and in need of help.

On May 3, 1846, Mexican artillery opened fire on the Fort and bombarded the men for two days. Their commanding officer, Maj. Jacob Brown, fell, mortally wounded and ammunition ran low. On the morning of May 5 the weary garrison found itself surrounded by thousands of Mexicans. Momentarily they expected the Mexican assault. The desperate men fired their signal guns all that day and night. On May 8th large numbers of the enemy were seen moving off in the direction of Point Isabel. Gen. Taylor had heard the gun and with reinforcements of 2,300 men was returning to relieve the fort. The Mexican army, numbering about 6,000 moved out to bar the road to the Fort and the two armies met face to face on an elevation known as the Palo Alto. For over an hour a cannon duel raged, and under cover of a dense cloud of black smoke, American artillery moved into a new position and opened a destructive fire on the right flank of the Mexican line of battle. Their barrage was deadly and the Mexican column was cut to pieces. In the growing dusk, the Mexicans attempted one last attack, but this too was repulsed. As the guns ceased to fire in the darkness the Mexicans fell back beyond the Palo Alto.

Our bandbox commemorates this moment in military history.

Battle of Chapultepec

This box commemorates the last decisive battle of the Mexican War. It depicts the charge of our troops against the formidable citadel of Chapultepec, a massive stone fortress atop a 200 foot rocky eminence situated about a mile south of Mexico City. At the time of the assault the fortress was serving as an elite military academy for teenage Mexican boys. Built in 1785, the stone castle served for some years as Montezuma's country estate before it was taken over by the military academy.

The approach to the city was through a marsh lowland, fortified by the Mexican general and dictator, Santa Ana, who at this point had taken personal command of his troops in the field. Two brisk and bloody actions were fought on the 19th and 20th of August, 1847, and the Mexicans were pushed back to their defenses just outside the city walls. General Winfield

Vignette depicts the heavy stone fortress of Chapultepec. Here the youngsters attending the military academy bravely defended it along with the regular forces.

Scott, commander of the American forces proposed an Armistice and Santa Ana agreed to discuss terms. However, it quickly became clear that the Mexicans were making use of the armistice talks as a breathing spell and so on September 6th Scott halted the discussions and prepared to assault the city. Two days later the most important outwork of Chapultepec was taken and on the 13th the citadel itself fell. That same night a small vanguard of Scott's troops pushed on and entered the gates of Mexico City. The Mexican authorities at dawn the next morning sent out the white flag. The garrison had slipped away during the night and it never rallied to become an effective fighting force again. Santa Ana abdicated the presidency and shortly afterwards the last remnant of his army, about 1,500 volunteers was completely defeated while trying to capture an American supply train on the road from Vera Cruz.

In February of 1848, the Treaty of Guadelupe Hidalgo was signed. Mexico ceded to the United States "Upper California," the present state of California and "New Mexico" which territory included the present states of Arizona, New Mexico, Utah, Nevada, a small corner of present-day Wyoming and the western and southern portions of Colorado. On its part, the United States agreed to pay Mexico $15,000,000 and to assume the unpaid claims against Mexico. The Rio Grande was officially recognized as the Texan boundary and on August 1, 1848, the last American soldiers stepped aboard their transports at Vera Cruz and quitted Mexican soil.

This pasteboard box is completely lined with a coarse cotton canvas, and has been covered with a block-printed paper in red, white, and blue on grey background.

View showing
Gen. Winfield Scott
directing the battle
for the fortress

17½ x 15½, 13″ deep

No. 94

Circa 1847

A Peep at the Moon

Mechanical difficulties have prevented the Air Force from achieving its exploration of outer space with a rocket to the moon. A century ago, however, the technicalities were not allowed to interfere with tidings from interstellar space. As proof we have a bandbox with its peep at the moon.

Pink, white and brown on a pale green background

18 x 14, 11½″ deep   No. 158   Circa 1840

What appears to be a miniature launching pad is in reality a telescope mounted on a skeleton framework. The telescope is trained on the moon which in its enormity dwarfs the mountains in the earthly landscape.

Life on the moon is plainly visible. The three aeronautical figures with wings dipping below their knees are engaged in what surely appear to be temporal pursuits. The seated figure seems to be introducing the two standing figures to each other. At this point they are about to shake hands. The lamb in the foreground can neither fly nor float, for he

Red, white and amber varnish on yellow background

19 x 11"   Panel No. 30   Circa 1840

wears no wings. Palm trees sway in the breeze and the volcano in the background spews forth its lunar lava.

Outer space matters a hundred years ago were of intense interest, just
as today they receive more than their share of newspaper headlines. Now
it is guided missiles, moon shoots and space exploration vehicles. At that
time it was sunspots, Orion nebula and the rings around Saturn that were
of absorbing importance.

In 1835 the comet observed by Edmund Halley in 1682 was again per-
ceived. Through the ages comets had been regarded with awe and terror.
Halley concluded that the comet under his observation must be the same
one written up and described in ancient history. He predicted the next
appearance of this comet would be about 1758 and that in 1835 it would
again be visible. When it actually did re-appear on schedule a giant step
forward in the history of heavenly bodies was taken.

The observatory at Harvard College was founded in 1839 and eight
years later a 15 inch telescope was installed there. At that time only one
other telescope in the world was as large.

Our "Peep at the Moon" also recalls one of the immortal journalistic
stunts—the Moon Hoax. This deception deluded the United States for
weeks and quintupled the circulation of the *New York Sun* in which the
articles first appeared in serial form. Written by Richard A. Locke in
1859, it set forth the "Discovery that the Moon has a Vast Population of
Human Beings." There was even an authentic view of the moon as an
illustration!

Acknowledgments

Special thanks are extended to the following learned people, all of whom have furnished basic information for this catalog: Miss Mary E. Dunn, of Nancy McClelland, Inc.; Miss Anne Herman and Mr. Whitfield of Jones & Erwin, Inc.; Mr. Calvin Hathaway, Director and Mr. H. L. Hotchkiss, Jr. of Cooper Union Museum; Mr. Erwin O. Christensen, Curator, Miss Judith S. Cousins and Mrs. Nancy L. Prigg of Index of American Design; Mrs. Frederick B. Wright, Pelham Manor, New York and Mrs. Levi P. Smith of Burlington, Vermont; Mr. J. Watson Webb, Jr., Los Angeles, California; Mr. George B. Farnham, Jaffrey Center, New Hampshire; Mr. R. W. G. Vail, Director, New-York Historical Society; Mr. Earle W. Newton, Director, Bureau of Museums, Harrisburg, Pennsylvania; Mr. Waverly P. Lewis, Devon, Connecticut; Mr. William E. Katzenbach, Palisades, New York; Mr. D. Graeme Keith, Mr. Clifford P. Monahon and Mr. L. Maxon of Providence, Rhode Island; Mr. Philip F. Purrington, New Bedford, Massachusetts; Mrs. Caroline Karpinski, Metropolitan Museum, New York; Mrs. Florence Paull Berger and Mr. J. Herbert Callister, Wadsworth Atheneum, Hartford, Connecticut; Mr. Eugene F. Kramer, Albany, New York; Miss Marion Hayes, New Haven, Connecticut and Mr. Kimball C. Elkins, Cambridge, Massachusetts.

We are also grateful to the chiefs in the rare book sections of reference libraries and their assistants who have verified dates and business listings in their old city directories. These include: Mr. Zoltan Haraszti and Mr. Louis Ugalde, Boston Public Library; Miss Ellen Shaffer and Miss Helen D. Subers, Free Library of Philadelphia; Mr. Marcus A. McCorison, Dartmouth College Library, Hanover, New Hampshire; Mr. Edward G. Freehafer and Mr. Gilbert A. Cam, New York Public Library; Miss Charlotte D. Conover, New Hampshire Historical Society Library, Concord, New Hampshire; Miss Fanny Howe, Troy New York Public Library; Miss Elizabeth Spring, Nashua New Hampshire Public Library and Miss Fannie Rothman of the Burlington Vermont Public Library.